LEVEL
3

motivation
MATH
COMMON CORE ALIGNED

student edition

W9-AZT-828

Critical Thinking for Life!
Mentoring Minds

Publisher
Michael L. Lujan, M.Ed.

Editorial Director
Teresa Sherman, B.S.E.

Production Coordinator
Kim Barnes, B.B.A.

Digital Production Artists
Sarah Poff, B.S.
Judy Bankhead, M.F.A.
Tammy McDaniel

Illustrators
Sarah DuPree, B.F.A.
Gabe Urbina

Content Development Team
Michael L. Lujan, M.Ed.
Teresa Sherman, B.S.E.
Marian Rainwater, M.Ed.
Karen White, M.Ed.
Stephanie Christian, M.Ed.
Jan Hood, M.Ed.
Jana Hunt, B.S.E.
Susan Rhoades, M.Ed.
Amy Walker, B.S.

Content Editorial Team
Allison Wiley, B.S.E.
Marian Rainwater, M.Ed.
Karen White, M.Ed.
Nancy Roseman, B.S.E.
Karen Reeves, M.Ed.
Stephanie Christian, M.Ed.
Chasity Wisenbaker
Jennifer Mallios, B.A.

This book has been lovingly dedicated to Melissa Maria Lujan.

Critical Thinking for Life!™
Mentoring Minds

P.O. BOX 8843 • Tyler, TX 75711

800-585-5258 • FAX: 800-838-8186
For other great products from Mentoring Minds,
please visit our website at:

MentoringMinds.com

ISBN: 978-1-935123-70-5

Motivation Math™, Student Edition

MOTIVATION MATH™
TABLE OF CONTENTS

Interpret Products of Whole Numbers (3.OA.1)..7

Interpret Whole-Number Quotients (3.OA.2)..13

Solve Word Problems: Multiplication and Division (3.OA.3)..19

Find the Unknown in Multiplication or Division Equations (3.OA.4)................................25

Apply Properties of Operations: Multiplication and Division (3.OA.5)..............................31

Understand Division as an Unknown Factor (3.OA.6) 37

Use Strategies to Multiply and Divide (3.OA.7)..43

Solve Word Problems: 2-Step, Using the Four Operations (3.OA.8) 49

Identify and Explain Arithmetic Patterns (3.OA.9)..55

Use Place Value to Round Numbers (3.NBT.1)..61

Add or Subtract Within 1000 (3.NBT.2) 67

Multiply 1-digit Numbers by Multiples of 10 (3.NBT.3)..73

Understand the Meaning of Fractions (3.NF.1)..79

Understand and Represent Fractions on a Number Line (3.NF.2)....................................85

Understand and Generate Equivalent Fractions (3.NF.3abc)..91

Compare Fractions (3.NF.3d)..97

Tell Time and Measure Time Intervals in Minutes (3.MD.1) 103

Estimate and Measure Liquid Volume and Mass (3.MD.2)..109

Draw Picture and Bar Graphs (3.MD.3) 115

Generate Measurement Data and Create Line Plots (3.MD.4)......................................121

Understand Area Measurement (3.MD.5)..127

Measure Area by Counting Unit Squares (3.MD.6) 133

Relate Area to Multiplication and Addition (3.MD.7)..139

Solve Problems with Perimeter (3.MD.8) 145

Classify 2-dimensional Shapes (3.G.1) 151

Partition Shapes into Equal Areas (3.G.2) 157

Chart Your Success 164

Math Glossary 167

Mathematics Chart 173

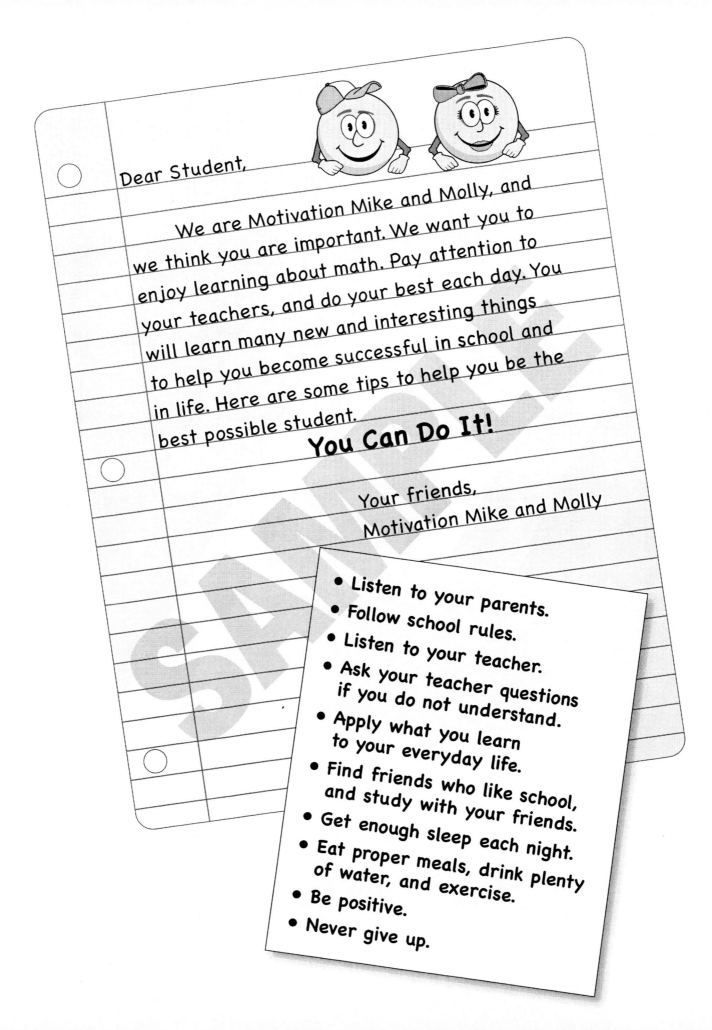

Dear Student,

We are Motivation Mike and Molly, and we think you are important. We want you to enjoy learning about math. Pay attention to your teachers, and do your best each day. You will learn many new and interesting things to help you become successful in school and in life. Here are some tips to help you be the best possible student.

You Can Do It!

Your friends,
Motivation Mike and Molly

- Listen to your parents.
- Follow school rules.
- Listen to your teacher.
- Ask your teacher questions if you do not understand.
- Apply what you learn to your everyday life.
- Find friends who like school, and study with your friends.
- Get enough sleep each night.
- Eat proper meals, drink plenty of water, and exercise.
- Be positive.
- Never give up.

1. Mrs. Witt has shadow boxes containing old soda bottle caps as shown. Each shadow box displays five soda bottle caps.

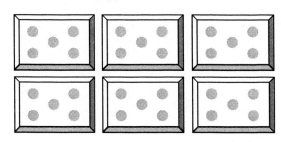

Write a multiplication equation that shows how many soda bottle caps Mrs. Witt has in her shadow boxes.

Answer: _____

2. Sonya invited eight friends to her birthday party. She gave each friend a party bag with five pieces of candy. Draw a picture showing Sonya's party bags and candy.

Write a multiplication equation to describe your picture.

Answer: _____

3. The city rose garden has three garden plots. Each plot contains nine rose bushes as shown in the picture.

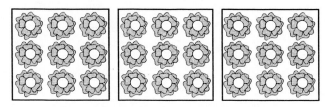

Write a multiplication equation that can be used to find how many rose bushes are in the three plots.

Answer: _____

4. Mia has seven chocolate chip cookies. Each cookie has six chocolate chips. Draw a picture showing the chocolate chip cookies.

Write a multiplication equation showing how many total chips are on the seven cookies.

Answer: _____

Words for the Wise

factor   multiplication   multiply   product

You shine!

★ **partner practice**

1. Ms. Eck placed plates of hot dogs on the table. Which set of plates shows 3×3?

Ⓐ

Ⓑ

Ⓒ

Ⓓ

2. Jimmy bought several small cartons of eggs. To find the total number of eggs purchased, he multiplied 3×6. Which of the following could describe the eggs Jimmy purchased?

Ⓐ Three cartons with six eggs in each carton makes a total of 18 eggs.

Ⓑ Six cartons divided into three groups results in two eggs in each group.

Ⓒ Two cartons of six eggs makes a total of 12 eggs.

Ⓓ Three cartons of 18 eggs is equal to a total of 54 eggs.

3. LaMark saw seven boxes of oranges at the grocery store. Each box had seven oranges as shown in the picture.

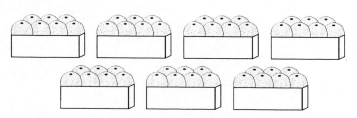

Which equation shows the total number of oranges LaMark saw?

Ⓐ $7 \times 9 = 63$

Ⓑ $7 \times 8 = 56$

Ⓒ $7 \times 7 = 49$

Ⓓ $6 \times 8 = 48$

4. Eduardo drew the picture below to show the multiplication equation $4 \times 8 = 32$.

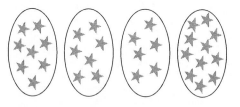

What mistake did Eduardo make?

Ⓐ Eduardo should have used a number line to show the problem.

Ⓑ Eduardo should have made eight groups of five stars.

Ⓒ Eduardo should have made each group contain eight stars.

Ⓓ Eduardo should have used an array to show the problem.

 Level 3

1. Connie collected ladybugs for her science class. She placed an equal number of ladybugs in each of her collection boxes. Which set of boxes shows 4 × 6?

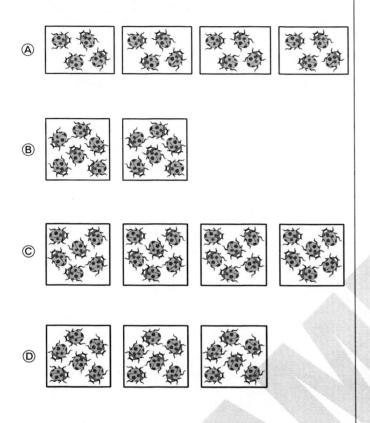

3. Ms. Campo has 5 boxes of crayons. Each box holds 9 crayons.

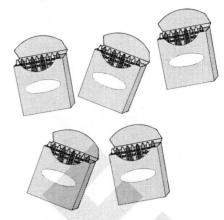

Which equation shows the total number of crayons in Ms. Campo's boxes?

Ⓐ $9 - 5 = 4$

Ⓑ $5 + 9 = 14$

Ⓒ $5 \times 8 = 40$

Ⓓ $5 \times 9 = 45$

2. Mario placed an equal number of baseball cards into each of 7 sandwich bags. To find the total number of baseball cards in all the bags, Mario multiplied 7 × 8. Which of the following could describe Mario's baseball cards?

Ⓐ 7 bags with 7 cards in each bag for a total of 49 cards

Ⓑ 7 bags with 8 cards in each bag for a total of 56 cards

Ⓒ 8 bags with 7 cards in each bag for a total of 56 cards

Ⓓ 8 bags with 8 cards in each bag for a total of 64 cards

4. Which of the following models does **not** show 3 × 10?

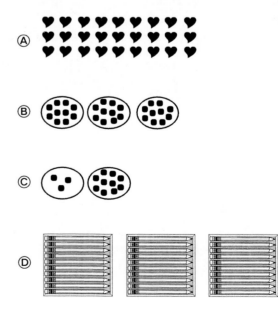

1. Kendra bought boxes of gingerbread cookies. There were an equal number of gingerbread cookies in each box. Which set of boxes shows 3×6?

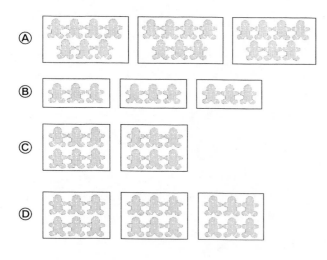

Ⓐ

Ⓑ

Ⓒ

Ⓓ

2. Sophie has 8 plastic boxes with an equal number of beads in each box. To find the total number of beads in all the boxes, Sophie multiplied 8 and 9. Which of the following could describe Sophie's beads?

Ⓐ 8 plastic boxes with 8 beads in each box for a total of 64 beads

Ⓑ 8 plastic boxes with 9 beads in each box for a total of 72 beads

Ⓒ 9 plastic boxes with 8 beads in each box for a total of 72 beads

Ⓓ 9 beads and 8 boxes for a total of 17

3. There are 4 shelves. Each shelf holds 7 books.

Which equation shows how many books are on all the shelves?

Ⓐ $4 + 7 = 11$

Ⓑ $7 \times 3 = 21$

Ⓒ $4 \times 7 = 28$

Ⓓ $7 \times 7 = 49$

4. Kendrick put the 24 coins from his coin collection into plastic coin boxes. He put an equal number of coins in each box. Which of the following could **not** describe Kendrick's coin boxes?

Ⓐ 3 boxes with 7 coins in each box

Ⓑ 4 boxes with 6 coins in each box

Ⓒ 6 boxes with 4 coins in each box

Ⓓ 8 boxes with 3 coins in each box

5. Sam drew the picture below to show the multiplication equation $5 \times 6 = 30$.

What mistake did Sam make?

_____

_____

 Level 3

Name _____

Application/Apply

1. Tracy's grandmother came to visit Tracy and her three sisters. She brought presents for the girls. She gave 5 hair bows to each girl. Draw a picture to show how many hair bows Tracy's grandmother brought the girls.

Write a multiplication equation that describes your picture. _____

Synthesis/Create

2. Create a multiplication word problem about this picture.

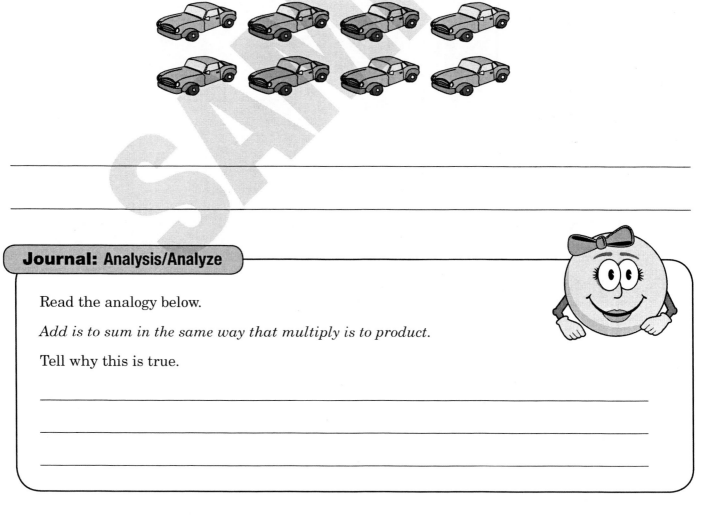

_____

_____

Journal: Analysis/Analyze

Read the analogy below.

Add is to sum in the same way that multiply is to product.

Tell why this is true.

_____

_____

_____

Tic-Tac-Toe

Play *Tic-Tac-Toe* using this game sheet and a pencil.

Solve each fact on the Tic-Tac-Toe grid. If the product is an even number, place an **E** in the box. If the answer is an odd number, place an **O** in the box. Three in a row wins the game.

6 × 2	3 × 5	4 × 6
7 × 5	5 × 5	2 × 4
3 × 3	1 × 0	6 × 5

5 × 9	3 × 4	7 × 1
8 × 2	7 × 7	3 × 8
4 × 3	10 × 0	9 × 3

10 × 2	0 × 8	3 × 7
7 × 5	4 × 8	6 × 6
3 × 1	9 × 9	5 × 9

8 × 8	6 × 9	9 × 1
10 × 10	7 × 9	9 × 10
3 × 9	1 × 0	8 × 5

Which letter won more games? _____

Parent Activities

1. Practice skip counting by 2s, 3s, 4s, 5s, and 10s.
2. Look at 4 pairs of shoes and show that 4 groups of 2 shoes equal 8 shoes. Challenge your child to find other equal groups of things (e.g., flowers in vases, eggs in egg cartons, apples in bowls).
3. Discuss the meanings of the words "double" and "triple."

1. Mrs. Vargas baked a dozen cookies for her 3 children to share equally. Draw a picture showing how many cookies each child received.

   Write an equation that describes your picture.

   Answer: _____

2. Tonya gathered flowers to make an arrangement for her mother's birthday. She noticed that each flower had 5 petals. She counted a total of 40 petals. Draw a picture showing how many flowers Tonya had in her arrangement.

   Write an equation that describes your picture.

   Answer: _____

3. The P.E. coach bought 20 feet of rope to make 4 jump ropes of equal length. Draw a picture showing how long each jump rope measured.

   Write an equation that describes your picture.

   Answer: _____

4. Emma bought 10 gumballs. She wants to separate them into groups of 2.

   Write a division equation showing the number of groups Emma should form.

   Answer: _____

Words for the Wise

| divide | division | equation | quotient |
| dividend | divisor | factor | |

Give it all you've got!

partner practice

1. Louise gathered 36 eggs from the hen house. She discovered that each of the 6 hens laid an equal number of eggs. Which equation shows how many eggs each hen laid?

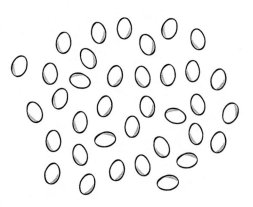

ⓐ 36 ÷ 4 = 9

ⓑ 36 ÷ 6 = 6

ⓒ 36 ÷ 12 = 3

ⓓ 36 + 6 = 42

2. Rolando baked 24 cookies and divided them into bags with 3 cookies in each bag. By finding 24 ÷ 3, Rolando knows how many people can receive a bag of cookies. Which of the following describes Rolando's cookies?

ⓐ Eight people each received 3 cookies. There were 24 cookies in all.

ⓑ Twenty-four bags of cookies were given to each of 8 people. There were 3 cookies per bag.

ⓒ There were 24 cookies in bags of 8. Each person received 3 cookies.

ⓓ Three people each received 8 cookies for a total of 24 cookies.

3. John is helping his mom put photographs in an album. Mom wants an equal number of pictures on each page. He knows there are 54 pictures, and the album has 9 pages. How can John determine the number of pictures to put on each page?

ⓐ add 54 and 9

ⓑ subtract 9 from 54

ⓒ multiply 54 and 9

ⓓ divide 54 by 9

4. Bernard made 20 pretzels to share with his friends. He and his 4 friends each ate the same number of pretzels. Which equation shows how many pretzels each person ate?

ⓐ 20 ÷ 2 = 10

ⓑ 20 ÷ 4 = 5

ⓒ 20 ÷ 5 = 4

ⓓ 20 + 4 = 24

 Level 3

1. Liz, Joe, Beth, and Ralph want to share 8 markers equally, so they divided 8 by 4. Which picture shows how many markers each child will get?

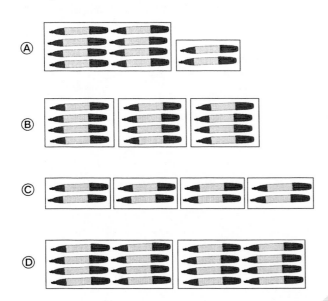

3. Jake wanted to prove that he could eat 3 French fries at a time. He ate a bag of 27 fries in this manner. What can Jake do to find out how many times he reached into the bag of fries?

Ⓐ He could multiply 3 by the number of fries in the bag.

Ⓑ He could divide 3 by 27.

Ⓒ He could divide 27 by the number of times he reached into the bag.

Ⓓ He could divide 27 by 3.

2. Candace collected 36 seashells. She wants to place them into bags with 9 shells in each bag. By solving 36 ÷ 9, Candace knows how many bags she needs for the shells. Which of the following correctly describes Candace's seashells?

Ⓐ There are 9 bags of shells with 4 shells in each bag for a total of 36 seashells.

Ⓑ There are 6 bags of shells with 6 shells in each bag for a total of 36 seashells.

Ⓒ There are 5 bags of shells with 9 shells in each bag for a total of 36 seashells.

Ⓓ There are 4 bags of shells with 9 shells in each bag for a total of 36 seashells.

4. Alex has 24 new marbles. He and his 3 friends share the marbles equally. Which equation shows how many marbles each child receives?

Ⓐ 27 ÷ 3 = 9

Ⓑ 24 ÷ 4 = 6

Ⓒ 24 ÷ 3 = 8

Ⓓ 24 − 3 = 21

★assessment

1. Central School's cafeteria has 12 gallons of milk to be shared equally among the third-grade classes. Each class receives 2 gallons of milk.

   Which equation can be used to find how many third-grade classes are at Central School?

   (A) 12 ÷ 3 = 4

   (B) 12 ÷ 4 = 3

   (C) 12 ÷ 2 = 6

   (D) 12 ÷ 1 = 12

2. Smiley the Clown brought 18 balloons to the party for the children to share equally. He gave each child 3 balloons. What can Smiley do to find the number of children at the party?

   (A) Divide 18 by 2.

   (B) Multiply 18 by 3.

   (C) Find the difference of 18 and 3.

   (D) Divide 18 by 3.

3. Sally planted 32 flowers in her grandmother's flower garden. She wanted to put an equal number of flowers in 4 rows. By dividing 32 by 4, Sally knew how many flowers to put in each row. Which of the following tells how many flowers were in each row?

   (A) Thirty-two flowers are planted in 8 rows with 4 flowers in each row.

   (B) Four rows of flowers each have 9 flowers. There are 32 flowers in all.

   (C) There are four rows of 32 flowers. There are 6 flowers in each row.

   (D) Thirty-two flowers are planted in 4 rows. There are 8 flowers in each row.

4. Yolanda made a pan of brownies to share with her 3 friends. She cut the brownies into 28 equal pieces. Which equation shows how many brownies Yolanda and her 3 friends get if they share the brownies equally?

   (A) 24 ÷ 3 = 8

   (B) 28 ÷ 4 = 7

   (C) 28 − 3 = 25

   (D) 28 + 3 = 31

5. Fifty-six people came to the Bratton family reunion. They wanted to divide into teams of 8 for relay races. Write and solve an equation that shows how many people will be on each team.

   Answer: _____

     Level 3

Analysis/Analyze

1. Paul has a package of bubble gum. He can divide his gum equally between two people with no pieces left over. He can also divide his gum equally between three people with no pieces left over. How many pieces of gum could Paul have in his package?

Explain how you found your answer.

_____

_____

_____

Synthesis/Create

2. Create a picture that shows dividing by 3.

What division equation matches your picture?

Answer: _____

Journal: Analysis/Analyze

Multiplication is a quick way to solve a repeated addition problem. $5 + 5 + 5$ is the same as 3×5. How is division like repeated subtraction?

_____

_____

_____

_____

motivation station

Musical Chairs

Mrs. Jones, the music teacher, has 24 chairs in her classroom. She arranges the 24 chairs differently for each grade. She makes 2 rows of chairs for the first graders. She makes 3 rows for the second graders, 4 rows for the third graders, 6 rows for the fourth graders, and 8 rows for the fifth graders.

Use color tiles to show the arrangement of chairs for each grade level.

Then, draw a picture to show how many chairs were in each row for each grade.

Grade	Picture	Number of Chairs Per Row
1st grade		
2nd grade		
3rd grade		
4th grade		
5th grade		

Which grade had the rows with the most chairs? _____

Which grade had the rows with the fewest chairs? _____

Parent Activities

1. After doing laundry, put all the socks in one pile. Practice division by saying, "There are 16 socks in all. How many pairs can we make?"

2. Using an egg carton and dried beans, have your child sort equal numbers of beans into the egg "cups." For example, put 24 beans equally into 6 cups. Then show how to write this as an equation. If 24 beans are divided equally into 6 cups, that equals 4 beans in each cup ($24 \div 6 = 4$). Repeat this activity for 12 cups, 8 cups, 4 cups, and 3 cups. As a variation, have your child use 30 beans and see how many cups can be filled if 3 beans are counted into each cup. Repeat with 5 beans, 6 beans, and 10 beans.

3. Have your child help divide a dozen cookies or brownies so that they can be shared equally with all members of the family. Depending on the number of family members, there may be nothing left over or there may be extra baked goods. Your child should be able to say and/or write an equation for the activity (e.g., 12 divided by 4 = 3 or 12 divided by 5 = 2 with 2 left over).

 Level 3

1. Bianca organized her seashell collection in the following array.

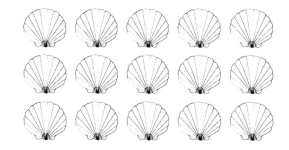

Write the equation that represents the arrangement of Bianca's array.

Answer: _____

2. Samantha has a frog named Croaker. Croaker moves 2 feet forward each time he hops. Use the number line to show how far Croaker would travel in 6 hops.

←—+—+—+—+—+—+—+—+—+—+—+—+—+—+—+—→
0 1 2 3 4 5 6 7 8 9 10 11 12 13 14 15
Feet

What equation can be used to describe the total distance Croaker traveled?

Answer: _____

3. Arnie, Matt, Craig, and Devon equally share the nuts in a canister of almonds. The canister contains 36 almonds. How many will each boy receive? Show your work.

Answer: _____

4. Two workers at Wiley Light Bulb Company place 30 light bulbs in boxes. They put 6 bulbs in each box. Draw a picture to show how many boxes the workers fill.

Write a division equation that describes your picture.

Answer: _____

5. Marissa purchased 3 bags of apples. There were 6 apples in each bag. How many apples did Marissa purchase? Write and solve an equation to find your answer.

Answer: _____

Marissa then gave 2 apples to each girl in her dance class and had no apples left over. How many girls are in Marissa's dance class? Write and solve an equation to find your answer.

Answer: _____

Words for the Wise

array	division	factor	product
divide	divisor	multiplication	quotient
dividend	equation	multiply	

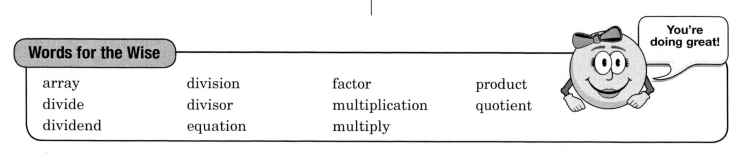

You're doing great!

partner practice

1. Lashonda cut a large pizza into 16 slices. Then she and her 3 brothers shared the slices equally.

Which equation shows how many slices each person received?

Ⓐ $16 \div 4 = 4$

Ⓒ $15 \div 3 = 5$

Ⓑ $16 \div 2 = 8$

Ⓓ $16 \times 3 = 48$

2. There are 8 rows on a checkerboard. Each row has 8 squares. How many squares are on a checkerboard?

Ⓐ 8

Ⓒ 46

Ⓑ 16

Ⓓ 64

3. Which of the following problems could be solved with the equation $54 \div 9 = \square$?

Ⓐ There are 9 trucks and 54 automobiles on the used car lot. How many vehicles are on the used car lot?

Ⓑ Tisha needs $54 to purchase a game. She has saved $9. How much more money does Tisha need to buy the game?

Ⓒ The students went on a trip to the science museum in 9 buses. Each bus carried 54 students. How many students went on the trip?

Ⓓ The YMCA formed teams for boys basketball. Each team had 9 boys. If 54 boys signed up to play, how many teams were formed?

4. At Brooks Grocery Store there are 6 types of canned vegetables for sale. There are 5 rows of canned corn with 7 cans in each row as shown in the picture below.

Which equation correctly shows how to find the total number of cans of corn for sale?

Ⓐ $6 \times 7 = 48$

Ⓒ $5 \times 7 = 45$

Ⓑ $5 \times 7 = 35$

Ⓓ $6 \times 7 = 42$

5. Zack and 8 of his friends went fishing. Each of the boys caught 2 fish. How many total fish did they catch?

Ⓐ 16

Ⓒ 18

Ⓑ 17

Ⓓ 19

6. Emilio made 6 short bookmarks and 5 long bookmarks from a spool of red ribbon. The short bookmarks were 6 inches (in.) long, and the long bookmarks were 8 inches long. How much ribbon did Emilio use for the short bookmarks?

Ⓐ 12 in.

Ⓑ 25 in.

Ⓒ 36 in.

Ⓓ 48 in.

 Level 3

1. Armand was playing a game. He measured and found that he could move forward 3 feet when he took a giant step. Armand took several giant steps as shown on this number line.

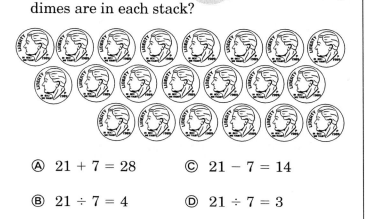

Which equation represents the total distance Armand moved with his giant steps?

Ⓐ 2 × 6 = 12

Ⓑ 3 × 3 = 9

Ⓒ 6 + 3 = 9

Ⓓ 4 × 3 = 12

2. The pizza man delivers 7 pizzas per hour. He works for 7 hours. How many pizzas will he deliver?

Ⓐ 140   Ⓒ 42

Ⓑ 49   Ⓓ 14

3. Robby has 21 dimes. He sorts the dimes into 7 equal stacks. Which equation shows how many dimes are in each stack?

Ⓐ 21 + 7 = 28   Ⓒ 21 − 7 = 14

Ⓑ 21 ÷ 7 = 4   Ⓓ 21 ÷ 7 = 3

4. Raymond has 24 flutes and 3 kazoos. He wants to put the flutes in boxes with 4 flutes in each box. Which equation shows how many boxes Raymond needs for the flutes?

Ⓐ 3 × 4 = 12

Ⓑ 24 ÷ 3 = 8

Ⓒ 24 ÷ 4 = 6

Ⓓ 23 + 3 + 4 = 30

5. Helen has 5 boxes of dog treats. Each box has 8 treats and weighs 6 ounces. How many dog treats does Helen have?

Ⓐ 20   Ⓒ 40

Ⓑ 30   Ⓓ 48

6. Which of the following could be solved using the equation 72 ÷ 9 = ☐ ?

Ⓐ There are 72 students in third grade. Coach Stinson put them in teams with 9 students on each team. How many teams did Coach Stinson form?

Ⓑ Angela gave each of the 72 students in third grade 9 gumdrops. How many total gumdrops did Angela give away?

Ⓒ Sylvia has 72 baseball cards. She gave 9 to her brother. How many cards does Sylvia have now?

Ⓓ Miguel has 72 coins in his collection. His grandfather gave him 9 more coins. How many coins are in Miguel's collection now?

★ assessment

1. Adrian's third-grade class went on a field trip to the park. The students collected 45 leaves and 36 rocks to share equally among 9 students. Which equation shows how many leaves each student received?

   (A) $45 + 36 = 81$ (C) $36 \div 9 = 4$

   (B) $45 \div 9 = 5$ (D) $45 \times 9 = 405$

2. Boppo and 5 other clowns are at the circus. Each clown carries 7 balloons. What is the total number of balloons carried by the clowns at the circus?

   (A) 12   (C) 42

   (B) 35   (D) 48

3. Tyler set a goal to read 5 books per month during the summer months of June, July, and August. How many total books should Tyler read during the summer to reach his goal?

   (A) 25   (C) 15

   (B) 20   (D) 5

4. Which of the following could be solved with the equation $56 \div 7 = \boxed{}$?

   (A) Ariel sold candy bars to raise money for her school. She started with 56 candy bars and sold all but 7 bars. How many bars did Ariel sell?

   (B) Mrs. Sorenson had 56 grapes. She shared the grapes equally among her 7 children. How many grapes did each child receive?

   (C) In his daily exercise program, Roger completed 56 sit ups. How many sit ups did Roger complete in one week?

   (D) On Tuesday morning there were 56 animals at the animal shelter. That afternoon, 7 more animals arrived at the shelter. How many animals were at the shelter then?

5. Elroy has a sheet of stickers containing 4 rows of stickers with 8 stickers in each row as shown below.

   Which equation shows the total number of stickers on the sheet?

   (A) $8 \div 4 = 2$ (C) $8 - 4 = 4$

   (B) $4 + 8 = 12$ (D) $4 \times 8 = 32$

6. Jenell purchased 4 cartons of juice with 6 bottles of juice in each carton. How many bottles of juice did Jenell purchase?

   Answer: _____

   Jenell then shared the juice with her class. She placed 3 bottles of juice on each table and had no bottles left over. How many tables are in Jenell's class?

   Answer: _____

 Level 3 ©2012–2014 MentoringMinds.com

Application/Apply

1. Bianca, Toffer, and Henry baked cupcakes for the bake sale. Henry baked 10 cupcakes. Toffer baked twice as many as Henry. Bianca baked triple the number that Toffer baked. How many cupcakes did Bianca bake?

Answer: _____

Analysis/Analyze

2. Shirley made sugar cookies. She plans to decorate the cookies with icing. She arranged them in 5 rows of 8 cookies to cool as shown.

When Shirley took the next batch of cookies out of the oven, she added 1 more row and 1 more column to her array of cookies that were cooling. How many cookies were cooling when the new batch was added?

Answer: _____

Write a division equation that is shown by the new array.

Answer: _____

Journal: Analysis/Analyze

How are factors and divisors alike?

_____

_____

_____

_____

Name _____

You Say, I Say

Play *You Say, I Say* with a partner. Decide which player is Player 1 and which is Player 2. In Round 1, Player 1 decides on a "secret rule" and records it on a scratch piece of paper so that Player 2 cannot see the rule. The rule must be to multiply or divide using a secret number. Player 2 then says and writes a number in the Round 1 table in the "You Say" column. Player 1 applies the secret rule to the number and says and writes the resulting number in the "I Say" column. Player 2 then says another number and Player 1 responds. Play continues in this manner for up to 5 numbers. At any point, Player 2 may try to guess the secret rule. If the first guess is correct, Player 2 scores 10 points. If the guess is incorrect, play continues. The next guess is worth 5 points. If Player 2 has not identified the rule in 2 guesses, Player 1 reveals the rule and scores 10 points. Players then reverse roles for Round 2.

Round 1

You Say	I Say

I think the secret rule is _____ .

Round 2

You Say	I Say

I think the secret rule is _____ .

You said 7 and I said 56. Do you know my secret rule?

I think I do! Is it multiply by 8?

Parent Activities

1. Use everyday opportunities such as ordering a pizza to help your child think mathematically. Ask questions such as, "If each member of the family eats 3 slices of pizza, how many slices do we need? If there are 8 slices per pizza, how many pizzas do we need to buy?"

2. Take advantage of displays in stores to point out multiplication. For example, a card of buttons could have 3 rows of buttons with 2 buttons in each row. Help your child see that 3 rows of buttons times 2 buttons in each row equals a total of 6 buttons.

3. Discuss words such as "double," "twice," "triple," "half," and "third" and how they apply to multiplication and division.

 Level 3

1. Lydia placed 42 books on a bookshelf with 6 shelves. She put the same number of books on each shelf. Complete the picture to show how many books Lydia placed on each shelf.

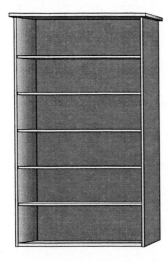

Complete the equation to describe your picture.

$$6 \times \boxed{} = 42$$

Answer: _____

2. Four girls and three boys shared 35 quarters equally. Draw a picture to show how many quarters each person received. Then complete the equation beneath your picture.

$$35 \div \boxed{} = 7$$

Answer: _____

3. Nine students in Ms. Hunter's room buy lunch every day. This equation can be used to find the number of lunches the cafeteria must prepare for Ms. Hunter's class each week.

$$\boxed{} = 9 \times 5$$

What is the missing number?

Answer: _____

4. Maria's teacher assigned a 15-page book report. Maria has 5 days to complete the assignment. She can use this equation to determine how many pages to complete each day.

$$? \times 5 = 15$$

What number makes Maria's multiplication equation true?

Answer: _____

5. The Johnson family is going on vacation to Hawaii. Mr. Johnson, Mrs. Johnson, and their 4 children can each carry three bags. The total amount of luggage they can bring is the missing number in this equation.

$$\bigstar \div 6 = 3$$

Find ★, the total number of bags the Johnson family can take to Hawaii.

Answer: _____

Words for the Wise

divide	fact family	product
equal (=)	factor	quotient
equation	multiply	whole number

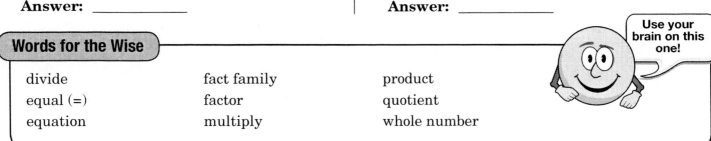

Use your brain on this one!

partner practice

1. Demarius had a rectangular cake. He needed to cut the cake into 30 equal slices. His mom cut the cake into 5 sections as shown.

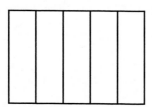

   Then his mom asked Demarius to finish cutting the cake. Demarius used this equation to decide how to divide each section.

   $$? \times 5 = 30$$

   Which number makes the equation true?

   Ⓐ 4   Ⓒ 25

   Ⓑ 6   Ⓓ 35

2. Don mows 12 yards each week. He mows every day except Sunday. Don used this equation to determine how many yards to mow each day.

   $$\_\_\_ = 12 \div 6$$

   Which number makes Don's equation correct?

   Ⓐ 24   Ⓒ 6

   Ⓑ 12   Ⓓ 2

3. A used car lot contains 10 cars. Johnny believes he can use this equation to find the number of tires on the cars in the lot.

   $$10 \times 4 = \bigstar$$

   Which number makes Johnny's equation true?

   Ⓐ 6   Ⓒ 24

   Ⓑ 14   Ⓓ 40

4. Darren has 7 bags of erasers with 9 erasers in each bag. To find the total number of erasers, Darren wrote this equation.

   $$? \div 9 = 7$$

   How many erasers does Darren have?

   Ⓐ 2   Ⓒ 56

   Ⓑ 16   Ⓓ 63

5. Dylan helped his teacher sort 24 sheets of paper. He put the paper in stacks of red, blue, and yellow. Each stack contained the same number of sheets. Dylan used this equation to calculate the number of sheets in each stack.

   $$24 = 3 \times \square$$

   Which is the correct number of sheets in each stack?

   Ⓐ 8   Ⓒ 12

   Ⓑ 10   Ⓓ 16

6. Jerri wrote this equation.

   $$5 \times ? = 45$$

   Which of the following does **not** describe this equation in words?

   Ⓐ Five groups of some number is the same as 45.

   Ⓑ Five groups of 45 is the same as the product.

   Ⓒ Five times some number is the same as 45.

   Ⓓ Multiplying 5 and a missing factor gives a product of 45.

Name _____

1. Trevor bought these 7 action figures for $56.

Each action figure cost the same amount. Trevor used the following equation to find how much he paid for each figure.

$$\$56 \div ? = 7$$

What was the cost of each action figure?

Ⓐ $8   Ⓒ $49

Ⓑ $9   Ⓓ $63

2. Pencils are sold in packages of 8. Ryan needed a total of 72 pencils. He used this equation to find the number of packages he needed to purchase.

$$8 \times \square = 72$$

How many packages of pencils did Ryan need to purchase?

Ⓐ 6   Ⓒ 9

Ⓑ 7   Ⓓ 80

3. The race car ride at an amusement park has 9 cars. Each car holds 4 people. The park manager uses this equation to find the total number of people who can ride the race cars at one time.

$$\_\_\_ \div 9 = 4$$

Which number makes the manager's division equation true?

Ⓐ 5   Ⓒ 36

Ⓑ 13   Ⓓ 54

4. Becky separated her 40 vocabulary flash cards into equal groups of 5, so she can study the same number of words each night. Becky used this equation to find how many words to study each night.

$$\_\_\_ = 40 \div 5$$

Which number correctly completes the equation?

Ⓐ 200   Ⓒ 10

Ⓑ 20   Ⓓ 8

5. Allison's mother baked a dozen cookies for Allison and her 3 friends to share. Allison wanted everyone to receive the same number of cookies. She used this equation to find the number of cookies each of them would receive.

$$12 = ? \times 4$$

Which unknown number makes the equation true?

Ⓐ 3   Ⓒ 9

Ⓑ 5   Ⓓ 36

6. Leo wanted to explain the following equation to his sister.

$$8 \times \_\_\_ = 56$$

Which of these would **not** be a correct description?

Ⓐ Eight groups of some number is the same as 56.

Ⓑ Fifty-six times an unknown number is equal to 8.

Ⓒ Eight times a number is the same as 56.

Ⓓ Multiplying 8 and a missing factor gives a product of 56.

     Level 3

★ **assessment**

1. Mr. Hughes is setting up chairs in the auditorium for the PTA program. There will be 9 rows of chairs with 6 chairs in each row. The total number of chairs in the auditorium can be determined by this equation.

$$\bigstar = 9 \times 6$$

How many chairs are in the auditorium?

Ⓐ 27

Ⓑ 36

Ⓒ 45

Ⓓ 54

2. Gina wants to make bracelets for 2 girls and 1 boy. She has 21 beads, and she wants to put an equal number of beads on each bracelet. Gina used this equation to find how many beads to use on each bracelet.

$$3 = 21 \div \,?$$

Which number makes Gina's division equation true?

Ⓐ 7

Ⓑ 8

Ⓒ 18

Ⓓ 21

3. Mrs. Oliver passed out pencils to 8 of her students. She has 40 pencils to give to the students, and each received the same number of pencils. Mrs. Oliver used this equation to find how many pencils to give each student.

$$40 = 8 \times \square$$

Which number makes this equation true?

Ⓐ 3

Ⓑ 4

Ⓒ 5

Ⓓ 6

4. Mrs. Waters wrote this equation on the board.

$$9 \times \underline{\quad} = 72$$

Which of the following does **not** describe this equation in words?

Ⓐ Nine groups of some number is the same as 72.

Ⓑ Nine groups of 72 is the same as the unknown number.

Ⓒ Nine times some number is the same as 72.

Ⓓ Multiplying 9 and a missing factor gives a product of 72.

5. Andrea and her 3 friends went to the Donut Palace to eat breakfast. Each girl ordered 2 plain and 2 chocolate donuts. The total number of donuts they bought is the missing number in this equation.

$$\square \div 4 = 4$$

What was the total number of donuts the girls bought?

Answer: _____

Level 3

Analysis/Analyze

1. Mr. Davidson took his wife and two children to see a movie last Saturday. He spent a total of $20 for tickets. An adult ticket cost $7. How much did a child's ticket cost?

Answer: _____

Explain how you found your answer.

_____

_____

_____

Synthesis/Create

2. Write a word problem that can be solved using the following equation:

$$36 = ? \times 4$$

_____

_____

_____

_____

Journal: Analysis/Analyze

Mrs. Jones wrote the numbers 6 and 3. She said, "These are two numbers in a fact family." Mrs. Jones asked the students to find the third number in the fact family.

Mathis said, "The third number is 2."

Tammy said, "The third number is 18."

Mrs. Jones said, "You are both correct."

Explain how this is possible.

_____

_____

_____

_____

Help Shayna get from her house to the park. Fill in the missing numbers.

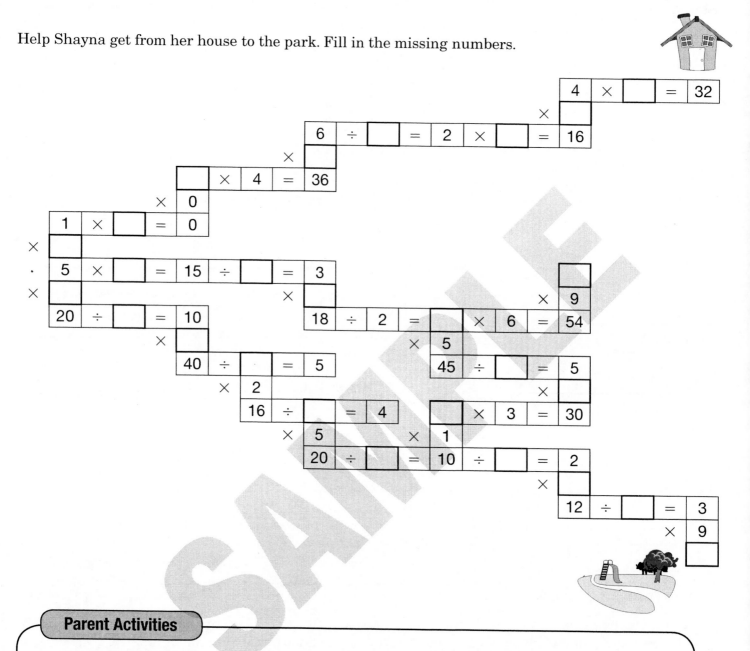

Parent Activities

1. Use a deck of cards with the face cards removed. Let the ace equal 1. Shuffle the cards and turn over the top 2 cards. Have your child multiply the 2 cards together and state the product. For example, if the top 2 cards are 7 and 4, your child states the product, 28. As a variation, turn over 2 more cards and put them together to make a 2-digit number, such as 56. Have your child tell you 2 numbers that could be multiplied to make that product.

2. Pop a small bag of popcorn. Count the number of popped pieces. Write an equation representing the amount of popcorn you would receive if you shared it with 1 friend. Repeat with 2 friends, 3 friends, etc.

3. Give your child a total of 45 dry beans. Ask him/her to arrange the beans in 9 equal groups. Then write the equation $45 \div ? = 9$. The number of beans per group is 5. Point out that $45 \div 9 = 5$, and also that $45 \div 5 = 9$.

Name _____

1. Mrs. Jones gives her students gold stars for good behavior. Freddie and Mil arranged their stars as shown.

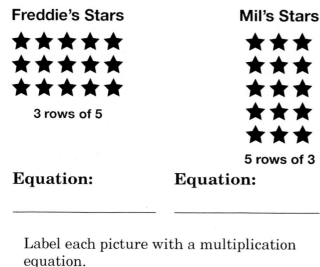

Freddie's Stars

3 rows of 5

Mil's Stars

5 rows of 3

Equation: **Equation:**

_____   _____

Label each picture with a multiplication equation.

Write a sentence comparing the two equations.

_____

_____

_____

2. Austin put away 28 towels. He made four stacks with 7 towels in each stack. Is it possible to stack the towels in 7 equal stacks?

Answer: _____

Explain your answer.

_____

_____

_____

3. Anna and Artur noticed an array in a display of pennies from Dad's coin collection. Anna sketched the array and used multiplication to find the total number of pennies in the display. Artur decomposed the array in his sketch and used multiplication to find the total a different way. Both children wrote equations below their sketches. Their work is shown.

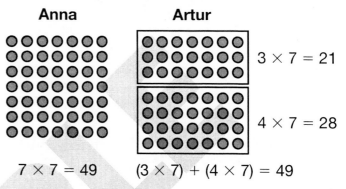

Anna   **Artur**

$3 \times 7 = 21$

$4 \times 7 = 28$

$7 \times 7 = 49$ $(3 \times 7) + (4 \times 7) = 49$

Draw rectangles to decompose this figure, showing another way to use multiplication to find the total number of pennies. Write the corresponding equation below your work.

Answer: _____

4. The product of $(5 \times 3) \times 6$ is 90. What do you know about the product of $5 \times (3 \times 6)$?

Answer: _____

_____

Words for the Wise

decompose   equation   expression   factor   product

You're catching on now!

⭐ **partner practice**

1. Which expression has the same value as 8×9?

Ⓐ $8 + 9$

Ⓑ $9 - 8$

Ⓒ 9×8

Ⓓ $9 \div 8$

2. Gage opened a bag of candies. He lined up the candies to show the product of 4×3 as shown.

○○○　○○○　○○○　○○○

Which group of candies shows Gage's product another way?

Ⓐ ○○　○○　○○　○○　○○

Ⓑ ○○○○○○○　○○○○○○○

Ⓒ ○○○○　○○○○

Ⓓ ○○○○　○○○○　○○○○

3. Mrs. Marco wrote the following equation on the board.

$$(2 \times 4) \times 6 = 48$$

Which of the following expressions has the same value?

Ⓐ $(2 \times 3) \times 7$

Ⓒ $2 + (4 \times 6)$

Ⓑ $2 \times (4 \times 6)$

Ⓓ $2 \times (4 + 6)$

4. Bailey and Lauren found the product of $2 \times 9 \times 4$. Bailey multiplied 18×4. Lauren multiplied another way. Which of the following could be a correct way that Lauren multiplied?

Ⓐ 9×6

Ⓒ 2×18

Ⓑ 4×36

Ⓓ 2×36

5. Lilly works at Colony Florist. On Friday, she received an order for 4 vases of flowers. The customer asked that each vase contain 7 red roses and 3 white roses. Lilly used the expression $4 \times (7 + 3)$ to find the total number of flowers she would need. Which of the following expressions has the same value as Lilly's expression?

Ⓐ $47 + 43$

Ⓒ $4 \times 7 \times 3$

Ⓑ $(4 \times 7) + (4 \times 3)$

Ⓓ $(4 \times 7) + (7 \times 3)$

6. Reggie collects football cards and baseball cards. He placed his cards in an array as shown. Then he wrote the equation $5 \times 7 = 35$ to show how many cards he has in all.

Which expression can help Reggie find the total number of cards in a different way?

Ⓐ $(3 \times 2) + 7$

Ⓒ $(5 \times 7) + (2 \times 7)$

Ⓑ $(2 \times 7) + (3 \times 7)$

Ⓓ $(2 \times 7) \times (3 \times 7)$

Level 3

1. Which equation is **not** correct?

   Ⓐ $3 \times 5 = 5 \times 3$

   Ⓑ $4 + 7 = 7 + 4$

   Ⓒ $10 \div 2 = 2 \div 10$

   Ⓓ $6 \times 8 = 8 \times 6$

2. For her birthday party, Shawna put cupcakes on a platter for her friends to enjoy.

   Shawna knew two ways to multiply to find the total number of cupcakes. One way was 3×5. Which expression shows another way?

   Ⓐ 5×3

   Ⓑ $5 + 3$

   Ⓒ $3 + 5$

   Ⓓ $5 \div 3$

3. Sienna solved $(2 \times 5) \times 3$ and found a product of 30. Which of the following is true about $2 \times (5 \times 3)$?

   Ⓐ The product is 2 times greater than 30.

   Ⓑ The product is less than 30.

   Ⓒ The product is 2 more than 30.

   Ⓓ The product is equal to 30.

4. Ethan read the following poem:

   As I was walking down the street
   A funny man I chanced to meet.
   Four heavy bags held in each hand;
   In each bag 3 pounds of sand.

   Which of the following could **not** be used to find the total number of pounds of sand the man carried?

   Ⓐ 2×12 Ⓒ 6×6

   Ⓑ 8×3 Ⓓ 4×6

5. Ruby made party bags to give to the friends at her birthday party. The 5 bags each had 2 pieces of gum and 3 sour drops. Ruby knew that the expression $(5 \times 2) + (5 \times 3)$ would show the total number of items in all the bags. Which expression also gives the total number of items in the bags?

   Ⓐ $(5 + 2) + 3$

   Ⓑ $5 \times (2 \times 3)$

   Ⓒ $(5 \times 2) - 3$

   Ⓓ $5 \times (2 + 3)$

6. Cole knew several ways to find the product in this equation.

   $$6 \times 12 = ?$$

   Which of the following could **not** be used by Cole to find the product?

   Ⓐ $(3 \times 12) + (3 \times 12)$

   Ⓑ $(6 \times 2) + (6 \times 6)$

   Ⓒ $(6 \times 10) + (6 \times 2)$

   Ⓓ $(6 \times 6) + (6 \times 6)$

★ assessment

1. Which equation is **not** correct?

   Ⓐ $(2 \times 3) \times 5 = 2 \times (3 \times 5)$

   Ⓑ $5 \times (4 + 8) = (5 \times 4) + (5 \times 8)$

   Ⓒ $6 \times 7 = 7 \times 6$

   Ⓓ $15 \div 3 = 3 \div 15$

2. Mandy solved $(2 \times 3) \times 6$ and found a product of 36. Which of the following is true about the expression $2 \times (3 \times 6)$?

   Ⓐ The product is less than 36.

   Ⓑ The product is 2 times greater than 36.

   Ⓒ The product is equal to 36.

   Ⓓ The product is 2 more than 36.

3. Ben's class has 3 rows of students with 5 students in each row. Each student has 4 pens. Ben said, "There are $3 \times 5 = 15$ students, so there are 15×4 pens." Which is another way to find the number of pens?

   Ⓐ $3 \times (4 + 5)$ Ⓒ $5 \times (3 + 4)$

   Ⓑ 3×20 Ⓓ 20×4

4. Each day Sara feeds her cats 3 scoops of dry cat food and 2 scoops of canned food. Sara knows that 7×3 is the number of scoops of dry food and 7×2 is the number of scoops of canned food the cats get in one week. Which expression shows the total number of scoops of food Sara's cats receive in one week?

   Ⓐ $(7 \times 3) \times (7 \times 2)$

   Ⓑ $7 \times (3 \times 2)$

   Ⓒ $7 \times (3 + 2)$

   Ⓓ $7 \times (3 - 2)$

5. Darienne is making 8 bags for a marble game. She wants each bag to contain 4 red marbles and 3 blue marbles. Which of the following shows a way that Darienne could find the total number of marbles she needs to buy for the game bags?

   Ⓐ $(8 + 4) \times (8 + 3)$

   Ⓑ $(8 \times 4) + (8 \times 3)$

   Ⓒ $(8 \times 4) + (3 \times 4)$

   Ⓓ $(8 \times 3) \times 4$

6. Four students were asked to use properties of multiplication and division to make equations. Their answers are shown on this chart.

Name of Student	Equation
Arnie	$3 \times 4 \times 5 = 12 \times 5$
Bennie	$4 \times 0 = 0 \times 4 = 0$
Cammie	$4 \times 12 = 12 \times 4$
Denny	$10 \div 2 = 2 \div 10$

   Which student's equation is **not** correct?

   Answer: _____

   Explain your answer.

   _____

   _____

 Level 3

Name _____

Analysis/Analyze

1. Read this riddle.

   A man was walking to his farm.
   He had 3 gift bags on each arm.
   Each bag contained 4 candy sweets
   To give his children special treats.

   Draw a picture in the box above to show the total number of treats the man was carrying.

   Showing all factors, write a multiplication equation that represents the problem. Solve for the total number of treats by grouping one pair of factors before multiplying.

   Answer: _____

   Group a different pair of factors and write the product. _____

   Compare the results of the two factor groupings.

   _____

Analysis/Analyze

2. Thomas had a difficult time remembering the product of 7×9, so he decomposed the fact into smaller facts as shown.

$$7 \times 9 = (7 \times 4) + (7 \times 5)$$
$$= 28 + 35$$
$$= 63$$

   What are two additional ways that Thomas can decompose 7×9 to find a product of 63?

Journal: Application/Apply

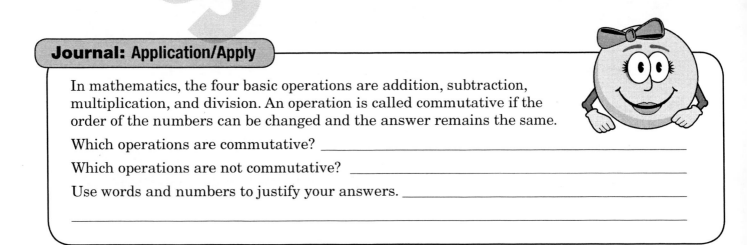

In mathematics, the four basic operations are addition, subtraction, multiplication, and division. An operation is called commutative if the order of the numbers can be changed and the answer remains the same.

Which operations are commutative? _____

Which operations are not commutative? _____

Use words and numbers to justify your answers. _____

_____

★ motivation station

Racing Rectangles

Play *Racing Rectangles* with a partner. Each player uses a game grid sheet. Each pair needs 2 number cubes. Player 1 rolls the cubes and draws 2 rectangles on the Round 1 grid, based on the numbers rolled. For example, if 6 and 3 are rolled, Player 1 draws one rectangle that is 6 by 3 and another rectangle that is 3 by 6. The player finds the sum of the areas of the two rectangles and records the score for the round. After 4 rounds, the player's score is determined by the sum of the areas of the rectangles on the 4 game grids. The player with the higher score wins.

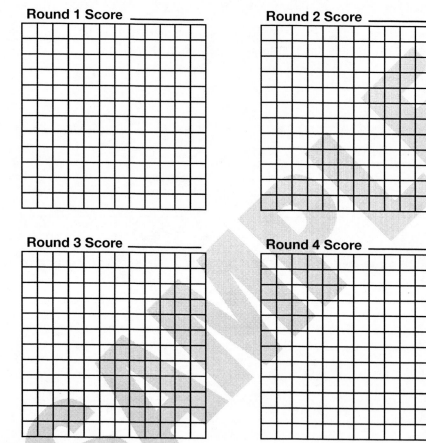

Round 1 Score _____

Round 2 Score _____

Round 3 Score _____

Round 4 Score _____

Parent Activities

1. Use plastic eggs to show that 6 rows of 2 eggs or 2 rows of 6 eggs are both equal to 12 eggs. Explore the other factors of 12, such as 3×4 and 4×3.

2. Create a rectangular pattern (called an array) with dried beans. Discuss the multiplication problem shown (e.g., 6 rows of 6 beans = 6×6). Next, use a piece of string to separate the beans into 2 smaller arrays (e.g., 2 rows of 6 beans and 4 rows of 6 beans). Discuss with your child how the sum of the two small arrays is equal to the large array. Record multiplication equations to verify (e.g., $(2 \times 6) + (4 \times 6) = 36$).

3. Remove the face cards and shuffle a deck of playing cards. Have your child draw 3 cards and form a multiplication expression (e.g., $4 \times 2 \times 6$). Solve by grouping the first 2 factors and multiplying (e.g., $(4 \times 2) \times 6 = 8 \times 6 = 48$). Then solve by grouping the second 2 factors before multiplying (e.g., $4 \times (2 \times 6) = 4 \times 12 = 48$). Point out that different groupings of factors yield the same product.

 Level 3

1. Look at the members of this fact family.

$6 \times 7 = 42$
$7 \times 6 = 42$
$42 \div 6 = 7$

   Write the equation that completes this fact family.

   Answer: _____

2. The computer lab has 24 desks in 3 equal rows. Write an equation that could be used to show the number of desks in each row.

   Answer: _____

   Write the other equations that belong to this fact family.

   _____

   _____

   _____

3. Kailey has 28 staples in her stapler. It takes 4 staples to hang one picture on her bulletin board. Kailey knows she can find the number of pictures she can hang by using the expression $28 \div 4$.

   Write a multiplication equation that Kailey could use to find the number of pictures she can hang.

   Answer: _____

4. Reese and 6 friends equally shared a package of 56 sports cards. How many sports cards did each person receive? Write the division equation you would use to solve this problem.

   Answer: _____

   Write a multiplication equation that helps you solve the division equation.

   Answer: _____

5. For a school project, Mrs. Wilson's class collected canned food for the food drive. Nine of her students brought the same number of cans for a total of 45 cans. To find how many cans each student brought, Mrs. Wilson divided 45 by 9. Write a multiplication equation that also shows how many cans each student brought.

   Answer: _____

6. Wayne plans to divide 32 baseballs equally into 4 boxes. Wayne knows that $4 \times 8 = 32$. Explain how Wayne can use this fact to find how many baseballs to put in each box.

   _____

   _____

   _____

Words for the Wise

divide	equation	inverse operations	
dividend	expression	missing factors	operation
division	fact family	multiplication	product
divisor	factor	multiply	quotient

The possibilities are endless!

★ partner practice

1. Denny used this array to model the multiplication equation $4 \times 8 = 32$.

Which division equation is modeled by the same figure?

Ⓐ $8 \div 2 = 4$ Ⓒ $24 \div 8 = 3$

Ⓑ $12 \div 4 = 3$ Ⓓ $32 \div 4 = 8$

2. The photographer placed 28 children in 4 equal rows. Which equation is in the same fact family as $28 \div 4 = \square$?

Ⓐ $28 \times 4 = \square$

Ⓑ $\square \div 4 = 28$

Ⓒ $28 \times \square = 4$

Ⓓ $4 \times \square = 28$

3. Which equation in the box does **not** belong in the fact family?

$$
\begin{array}{rcl}
8 \times 6 & = & 48 \\
6 \times 8 & = & 48 \\
48 \div 12 & = & 4 \\
48 \div 8 & = & 6
\end{array}
$$

Ⓐ $8 \times 6 = 48$

Ⓑ $6 \times 8 = 48$

Ⓒ $48 \div 12 = 4$

Ⓓ $48 \div 8 = 6$

4. Ike wants to separate his 24 action figures equally into 3 boxes. He wrote this equation to find how many figures to put in each box.

$$24 \div 3 = ?$$

Which of the following equations can help Ike find the quotient?

Ⓐ $4 \times 6 = 24$ Ⓒ $2 \times 12 = 24$

Ⓑ $3 \times 8 = 24$ Ⓓ $24 - 3 = 21$

5. Pete's Pet Store divided 45 hamsters so that 5 hamsters were placed in each cage. Pete wrote this equation to show how many cages were needed.

$$45 \div 5 = 9$$

Which expression might Pete have used to find this quotient?

Ⓐ 5×9

Ⓑ $5 \div 45$

Ⓒ $45 - 9$

Ⓓ 45×5

6. Coach Allen ordered 30 new balls for his P.E. program. He ordered equal numbers of soccer balls, basketballs, and volleyballs. Which shows related facts that can be used to find how many of each type ball Coach Allen ordered?

Ⓐ $5 \times 6 = 30, \ 30 \div 5 = 6$

Ⓑ $3 \times 9 = 27, \ 27 \div 3 = 9$

Ⓒ $3 \times 10 = 30, \ 30 \div 3 = 10$

Ⓓ $2 \times 15 = 30, \ 30 \div 2 = 15$

1. Wilton used an area model to show the division equation $20 \div \boxed{} = 4$.

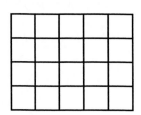

Which multiplication equation is modeled by the same figure?

Ⓐ $4 \times \boxed{} = 20$

Ⓑ $\boxed{} \times 4 = 16$

Ⓒ $4 \times \boxed{} = 24$

Ⓓ $\boxed{} \times 20 = 4$

2. Maggie and her 2 sisters bought a scarf for their mother. The scarf cost $24, and they shared the cost equally. Which equation is in the same fact family as $24 \div 3 = \boxed{}$?

Ⓐ $4 \times \boxed{} = 24$

Ⓑ $\boxed{} \times 3 = 24$

Ⓒ $24 \div 2 = \boxed{}$

Ⓓ $24 \times 3 = \boxed{}$

3. Sherri and 5 friends purchased 3 dozen cookies. They divided the cookies equally. Which shows the related facts that can be used to determine how many cookies each person receives?

Ⓐ $7 \times 5 = 35,\ 35 \div 5 = 7$

Ⓑ $6 \times 6 = 36,\ 36 \div 6 = 6$

Ⓒ $5 \times 5 = 25,\ 25 \div 5 = 5$

Ⓓ $3 \times 5 = 15,\ 15 \div 5 = 3$

4. Olivia is equally dividing 56 buttons to sew on 7 coats. Which of the following is another way to find $56 \div 7$?

Ⓐ $56 \times \underline{} = 7$

Ⓑ $56 \times 7 = \underline{}$

Ⓒ $7 \times 7 = \underline{}$

Ⓓ $7 \times \underline{} = 56$

5. Mitch and Missy practice multiplication and division facts using triangular flash cards. Which fact is **not** in the family of facts for this flash card?

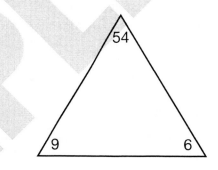

Ⓐ $9 \times 6 = 54$

Ⓑ $54 \div 6 = 9$

Ⓒ $9 + 6 = 15$

Ⓓ $54 \div 9 = 6$

6. The school nurse has 36 thermometers. She put an equal number of thermometers in 4 boxes. Which equation could **not** be used to find how many thermometers are in each box?

Ⓐ $36 \div 4 = \boxed{}$

Ⓑ $4 \times \boxed{} = 36$

Ⓒ $36 \div \boxed{} = 4$

Ⓓ $36 \times 4 = \boxed{}$

1. Shonda used this array to model the multiplication equation $\boxed{} \times 10 = 30$.

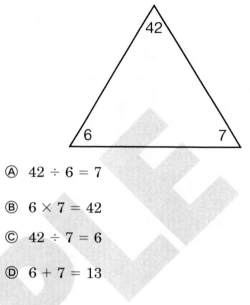

Which of the following is also modeled by Shonda's array?

Ⓐ $30 \div 6 = \boxed{}$ Ⓒ $30 \times 3 = \boxed{}$

Ⓑ $30 \div \boxed{} = 3$ Ⓓ $30 \div \boxed{} = 5$

2. Mrs. Ward bought a box of 64 pencils to be shared equally by her 8 children. Which equation is in the same fact family as $64 \div 8 = \boxed{}$?

Ⓐ $8 \times \boxed{} = 64$ Ⓒ $8 + \boxed{} = 64$

Ⓑ $64 - 8 = \boxed{}$ Ⓓ $64 \times 8 = \boxed{}$

3. Sue and three friends ordered a total of 40 rolls of wrapping paper. Each girl ordered an equal number of rolls. Which shows related facts that can be used to find how many rolls of paper each girl ordered?

Ⓐ $4 \times 10 = 40, \quad 40 \div 4 = 10$

Ⓑ $5 \times 8 = 40, \quad 40 \div 5 = 8$

Ⓒ $36 + 4 = 40, \quad 40 - 4 = 36$

Ⓓ $36 \div 4 = 9, \quad 4 \times 9 = 36$

4. Jay and Ken are practicing multiplication and division fact families using triangular flash cards. Which fact is **not** in the family of facts for this card?

Ⓐ $42 \div 6 = 7$

Ⓑ $6 \times 7 = 42$

Ⓒ $42 \div 7 = 6$

Ⓓ $6 + 7 = 13$

5. Cassandra knows that it takes her 7 minutes to walk 1 lap around the track. She wants to know how many laps she can walk in 63 minutes. Cassandra decides to divide 63 by 7 to find her answer. Which shows a related fact that can help Cassandra find the quotient?

Ⓐ $7 + 1 = 8$

Ⓑ $7 \times 6 = 42$

Ⓒ $9 \times 7 = 63$

Ⓓ $8 \times 7 = 56$

6. Jeremiah said that 54 divided by 6 is 9. What multiplication fact can Jeremiah use to check his work?

Answer: _____

Level 3   ©2012–2014 MentoringMinds.com

Analysis/Analyze

1. Explain how this triangular flash card could be used to illustrate a fact family.

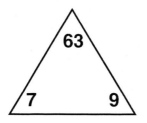

_____

_____

Analysis/Analyze

2. Lane wrote two numbers from a fact family. The numbers were 4 and 12. What is the other number in this fact family?

Answer: _____

Can you think of another fact family that contains 4 and 12?

Answer: _____

Explain how you found your answer.

_____

_____

_____

Journal: Analysis/Analyze

Alice wrote this fact family.

$4 \times 0 = 0$ $0 \div 0 = 4$

$0 \times 4 = 0$ $0 \div 4 = 0$

Use words or pictures to explain the mistake in Alice's equations.

_____

_____

_____

★ motivation station

Find the quotients for the division problems in the picture below. Then color each section using the key.

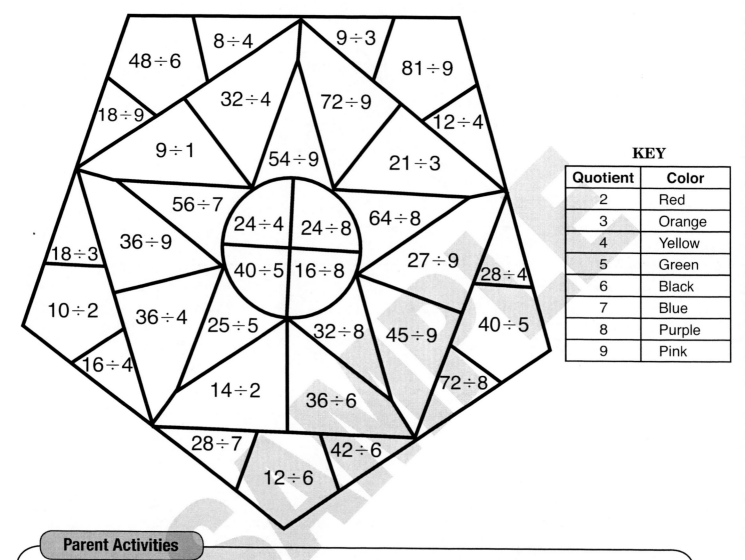

KEY

Quotient	Color
2	Red
3	Orange
4	Yellow
5	Green
6	Black
7	Blue
8	Purple
9	Pink

Parent Activities

1. Have your child use pennies to make rows that you specify. For example, have your child make 4 rows of 5 pennies and tell the total number of pennies. Next have your child make 5 rows of 4 pennies and tell the total number of pennies. Discuss that 4×5 and 5×4 have the same product. They belong to the fact family of 4, 5, and 20.

2. Have your child take 20 pennies and divide them into 4 equal piles and tell how many pennies are in each pile. Next have your child divide the pennies into 5 equal piles and tell how many pennies are in each pile. Point out that $20 \div 4 = 5$ and $20 \div 5 = 4$. These are part of the same fact family of 4, 5, and 20.

3. Work with your child to make a large rectangle with a length of 4 square Post-it® notes and a width of 2 notes. Show your child how four members of a fact family can be written using the length, width, and area of the large rectangle: $4 \times 2 = 8, 2 \times 4 = 8$, $8 \div 4 = 2, 8 \div 2 = 4$.

4. State a division problem, and have your child respond with the appropriate multiplication fact. For example, if you say $54 \div 9$, your child responds with $9 \times 6 = 54$.

Name _____

1. The product of 2 and 6 is 12. Name two other factors that also have a product of 12.

Answer: _____

2. The quotient of 30 divided by 6 is 5. Name two more division facts that have a quotient of 5.

Answer: _____

_____

3. Complete the following multiplication facts.

$2 \times 9 =$ _____ $6 \times 9 =$ _____

$3 \times 9 =$ _____ $7 \times 9 =$ _____

$4 \times 9 =$ _____ $8 \times 9 =$ _____

$5 \times 9 =$ _____ $9 \times 9 =$ _____

Describe a pattern you see in the products.

Answer: _____

_____

_____

4. Miss Baker's classroom has 7 rows of desks with 8 desks in each row. Write an equation that shows how many desks are in the room.

Answer: _____

5. There are 45 third-grade students. Mrs. Reyna, the music teacher, arranges the students in 5 equal rows on the stage. How many students are in each row?

Answer: _____

6. Carter bought 16 batteries for his remote control trucks. Each truck needed 2 batteries. How many remote control trucks does Carter have?

Answer: _____

7. Marsha's grandmother has 7 hummingbird feeders in her backyard. She counts 4 birds at each feeder. Write a multiplication fact that shows the total number of hummingbirds at the feeders.

Answer: _____

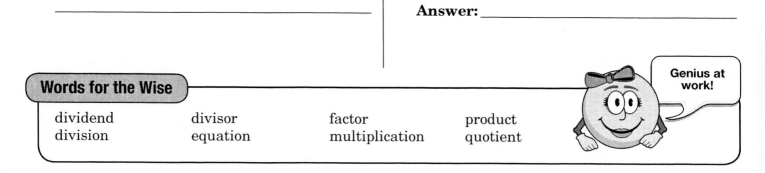

Words for the Wise

Genius at work!

| dividend | divisor | factor | product |
| division | equation | multiplication | quotient |

partner practice

1. Which fact has the same product as 6×6?

   Ⓐ 7×5

   Ⓑ 9×3

   Ⓒ 7×4

   Ⓓ 4×9

2. Which fact does **not** have the same quotient as $42 \div 7$?

   Ⓐ $24 \div 4$

   Ⓑ $30 \div 5$

   Ⓒ $56 \div 8$

   Ⓓ $54 \div 9$

3. Randy practices basketball after school. Before taking a practice shot, Randy always dribbles the ball 5 times. Randy makes 6 practice shots. How many times does he dribble the ball?

   Ⓐ 24

   Ⓑ 30

   Ⓒ 36

   Ⓓ 42

4. Xavier arranged 56 trophies on the 8 shelves in his room. He put the same number on each shelf. How many trophies did Xavier place on each shelf?

   Ⓐ 7

   Ⓑ 8

   Ⓒ 48

   Ⓓ 64

5. Carnations are sold in bunches of 6. Rory bought 3 bunches of carnations for his teachers. His brother, Clyde, bought 4 bunches of carnations. How many carnations did the two brothers buy altogether?

   Ⓐ 18

   Ⓑ 36

   Ⓒ 42

   Ⓓ 48

6. It is feeding time at the city zoo. The zookeeper has 16 bananas to share equally among the four gorillas. How many bananas does each gorilla receive?

   Ⓐ 3

   Ⓑ 4

   Ⓒ 12

   Ⓓ 20

 Level 3

1. Which fact has the same product as 3×8?

   Ⓐ 2×9

   Ⓑ 7×3

   Ⓒ 6×4

   Ⓓ 5×5

2. Which fact does **not** have the same quotient as $64 \div 8$?

   Ⓐ $32 \div 4$

   Ⓑ $40 \div 5$

   Ⓒ $56 \div 7$

   Ⓓ $54 \div 6$

3. Chantel and her cousin skipped smooth stones across the lake. Chantel threw a stone that made 6 skips. Each skip covered 7 feet as shown on this number line.

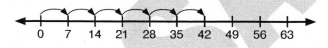

Which equation can be used to find how far Chantel's stone traveled?

   Ⓐ $7 \times 7 = 42$

   Ⓑ $6 \times 7 = 42$

   Ⓒ $6 + 36 = 42$

   Ⓓ $35 \div 7 = 5$

4. Elsa looked at the fish in the pet store. She counted exactly 8 fish in each aquarium. There were 9 aquariums. What was the total number of fish in the aquariums?

   Ⓐ 63

   Ⓑ 64

   Ⓒ 72

   Ⓓ 81

5. Mrs. Yen has 25 dimes. She gives the same number of dimes to each of her 5 children. How many dimes will each child receive?

   Ⓐ 4

   Ⓑ 5

   Ⓒ 6

   Ⓓ 7

6. The post office has 27 packages to be delivered. There are 9 mail carriers who each receive the same number of packages to deliver. How many packages does each mail carrier deliver?

   Ⓐ 3

   Ⓑ 4

   Ⓒ 5

   Ⓓ 6

★ assessment

1. Which fact has the same product as 2×9?

   Ⓐ 4×4 Ⓒ 7×3

   Ⓑ 6×3 Ⓓ 4×5

2. Which fact does **not** have the same quotient as $63 \div 7$?

   Ⓐ $48 \div 6$ Ⓒ $45 \div 5$

   Ⓑ $36 \div 4$ Ⓓ $72 \div 8$

3. Lilly bought 24 fish at Pet Station. She divided them equally into 1 glass aquarium and 2 plastic aquariums. How many fish did Lilly put in each aquarium?

   Ⓐ 12   Ⓒ 6

   Ⓑ 8   Ⓓ 3

4. Grant has 7 cans of new tennis balls for his first lesson. There are 3 balls in each can. How many tennis balls does Grant have?

   Ⓐ 4

   Ⓑ 14

   Ⓒ 18

   Ⓓ 21

5. Bruce had 35 ants. He divided them equally into 5 different jars. How many ants did Bruce put in each jar?

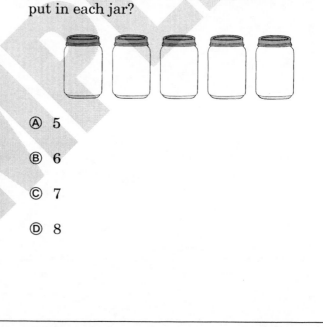

   Ⓐ 5

   Ⓑ 6

   Ⓒ 7

   Ⓓ 8

6. For reading the most books during the month of September, the third-grade classes at Waring Elementary were given a pizza party. Mrs. Smith's class had 3 pizzas, and Mrs. Allen's class had 4 pizzas. Each pizza had 8 slices. How many total slices of pizza did the 2 classes have? Show your work.

   Answer: _____

     Level 3

Analysis/Analyze

Use the hundred chart to skip count as outlined below.

• Draw a red circle around the numbers you say when you skip count by 3.

• Draw a blue square around the numbers you say when you skip count by 4.

• Draw a green triangle around the numbers you say when you skip count by 5.

1	2	3	4	5	6	7	8	9	10
11	12	13	14	15	16	17	18	19	20
21	22	23	24	25	26	27	28	29	30
31	32	33	34	35	36	37	38	39	40
41	42	43	44	45	46	47	48	49	50
51	52	53	54	55	56	57	58	59	60
61	62	63	64	65	66	67	68	69	70
71	72	73	74	75	76	77	78	79	80
81	82	83	84	85	86	87	88	89	90
91	92	93	94	95	96	97	98	99	100

Use words to describe the patterns you see on the hundred chart.

_____

_____

_____

_____

Journal: Analysis/Analyze

The Commutative Property of Multiplication tells us that changing the order of the factors does **not** change the product. For example, $5 \times 9 = 45$ and $9 \times 5 = 45$.

How can understanding this property help you memorize multiplication facts?

_____

_____

_____

Continental Divide

Play *Continental Divide* with a friend. Each player needs a small game marker such as a centimeter cube. Each pair of players needs a number cube and the game board. Determine which player will go first. The first player rolls the number cube and moves along the path, starting in California and traveling towards Florida. The player must correctly answer the fact in each space as he/she moves along the path. If an error is made, the player must return to the starting space for that turn. Play alternates between Player 1 and Player 2. Player 2 begins the game in Florida and travels along the path toward California. The winner is the first player to make the cross-country journey.

$7\overline{)56}$	2×6	$81 \div 9$	3×9					
4×8			**Advance 2 Spaces**					
Go Back 3 Spaces	$2\overline{)0}$		$24 \div 8$	$9\overline{)36}$	7×7	$8\overline{)8}$		
	7×5		5×9	8×1		7×9		
	$18 \div 6$		$6\overline{)36}$	$28 \div 4$		$48 \div 8$		
	8×8		8×9	8×4		**Go Back 4 Spaces**	9×2	$3\overline{)24}$
PLAYER 1 Begins	$4\overline{)36}$		$40 \div 8$	**Advance 3 Spaces**				6×6
			5×4	$1\overline{)6}$	5×5	$6\overline{)54}$		$56 \div 8$
			Lose A Turn			3×3		9×7
			$45 \div 9$	9×8	$40 \div 5$	$30 \div 6$		**PLAYER 2 Begins**
					6×8	4×4		
					$7\overline{)49}$	6×7	$9\overline{)54}$	

Parent Activities

1. Practice multiplication and division facts regularly with your child using flash cards or multiplication charts.

2. Practice skip counting by 2s, 3s, 4s, 5s, and 10s. These multiples will help your child recognize products.

3. Turn dominoes face down. Have your child turn over one domino and multiply the numbers on each end of the domino. Record a multiplication equation for that fact, and then have your child give a corresponding division equation (e.g., $4 \times 6 = 24$ and $24 \div 4 = 6$).

 Level 3

1. Mrs. Tremain wants to run 100 kilometers during the first three months of the year. In January she ran 24 kilometers, and in February she ran 37 kilometers. How many kilometers does Mrs. Tremain need to run in March in order to meet her goal? Write an equation that can be used to solve the problem and find the answer.

Answer: _____

2. There are 79 students in the third grade at Wilson Elementary School. Mrs. Henry's class has 12 boys and 11 girls. Katy estimated the number of students who were not in Mrs. Henry's class. She rounded all the numbers in the problem and found an answer of about 60. Is Katy's estimate reasonable? How do you know?

Answer: _____

_____

_____

3. Arnell collected bugs for a science fair project. He knows that insects each have 6 legs and spiders each have 8 legs. Arnell collected 7 insects and 1 spider. How many total legs do the bugs in Arnell's bug collection have? Show all work.

Answer: _____

4. Teri Kay is helping her mother organize the pantry. There are 6 shelves in the pantry. Each shelf can hold 20 cans of food. She put a total of 49 cans of food on the shelves. How many more cans will Teri Kay be able to put on the shelves in the pantry? Show all work.

Answer: _____

5. Lisa wrote the beginning of a word problem that could be solved using this equation, but she was interrupted and forgot to finish her problem.

$$282 - 86 + 114 = n$$

The beginning of Lisa's word problem was:

Marcy had 282 coins in her coin collection. She sold 86 coins at a coin show. Then…

Finish Lisa's word problem.

Answer: _____

_____

_____

6. Dell wants to buy filler pages for his sports card album. He knows that each page holds 6 sports cards. Dell has 15 basketball cards and 9 hockey cards. How can Dell determine how many filler pages he needs for his sports cards?

Answer: _____

_____

_____

Words for the Wise

addition	equation	reasonable
compatible numbers	estimate	round
division	multiplication	subtraction

Give me a high five!

★ partner practice

1. What is the total number of sides on eight octagons and seven hexagons?

Ⓐ 99   Ⓒ 113

Ⓑ 106   Ⓓ 200

2. Laura made two pans of brownies. She cut each pan into 20 brownies. Her friends ate 24 brownies. How many brownies were left?

Ⓐ 54   Ⓒ 16

Ⓑ 41   Ⓓ 7

3. Tyler's family drove 864 miles to Washington, D. C., over a 3-day period. On the first day they drove 283 miles. The second day they drove 307 miles. Tyler decided to estimate how far the family still had to travel on the third day. Which of the following is reasonable if Tyler used the rounding strategy to estimate the answer?

Ⓐ Tyler found the sum of 200 and 300. He subtracted this from 900 miles. Tyler reported that the family still needed to travel about 400 miles.

Ⓑ Tyler found the sum of 300 and 300 and added this to 900 miles. Tyler reported that the family still needed to travel about 1500 miles.

Ⓒ Tyler found the sum of 300 and 300 and divided this by 3. Tyler reported that the family still needed to travel about 200 miles.

Ⓓ Tyler found the sum of 300 and 300. He then found the difference between 900 and 600. He reported that the family still needed to travel about 300 miles.

4. A group of 6 children and 3 adults went to a movie matinee where all tickets cost \$6. The group used this equation to find their total bill.

$$\boxed{} = (6 + 3) \times \$6$$

How much did the group pay for movie tickets?

Ⓐ \$6

Ⓑ \$18

Ⓒ \$36

Ⓓ \$54

5. Sarah ate 17 potato chips, 53 raisins, and 14 pretzels for a snack. Which equation could be used to estimate how many more raisins Sarah ate than potato chips and pretzels combined?

Ⓐ $? = 50 - 20 - 10$

Ⓑ $? = 60 - 20 + 10$

Ⓒ $? = 60 + 20 + 10$

Ⓓ $? = 20 + 20 + 50$

6. Meg is counting the change in her purse. She has nine nickels and three dimes. What is the value of the money in Meg's purse?

Ⓐ 65¢

Ⓑ 75¢

Ⓒ 80¢

Ⓓ 85¢

     Level 3

1. Daphne bought 8 packages of paper plates for a picnic. The total cost of the plates was $32. She realized that she did not have enough plates, so she returned to the store and bought an additional package of paper plates. How much money did Daphne spend for all the paper plates?

Ⓐ $4

Ⓑ $33

Ⓒ $36

Ⓓ $40

2. Most apples contain 5 seed pockets called carpels. Each carpel contains 2 apple seeds. Which equation would best describe the total number of seeds in 10 apples?

Ⓐ $10 + 5 \times 2 = 30$

Ⓑ $10 + 2 \times 5 = 60$

Ⓒ $5 + 2 \times 10 = 70$

Ⓓ $5 \times 2 \times 10 = 100$

3. A ticket seller at a theater sold tickets for a school play. He sold 412 tickets for Section A and 378 tickets for Section B. He also sold 161 tickets for the balcony. About how many fewer tickets were sold for the balcony than for Sections A and B combined?

Ⓐ 600

Ⓑ 700

Ⓒ 800

Ⓓ 1000

4. Mindy and the 7 girls in her scout troop each pledged to collect 80 cans of food for the food drive. All the girls met their goal, but Mindy collected an additional 36 cans of food. How many cans of food did the girls in the scout troop collect?

Ⓐ 676

Ⓑ 604

Ⓒ 596

Ⓓ 116

5. Which of the following could be solved using this equation?

$$(17 + 32) \div 7 = 7$$

Ⓐ Last week, Rudy earned $17 raking leaves and $32 mowing lawns. How much money did Rudy earn last week?

Ⓑ Rudy had 17 baseball cards. His uncle gave him 32 more cards. Rudy bought 7 cards from his friend Chen. How many baseball cards does Rudy have now?

Ⓒ In one week, Rudy swims 17 miles and rides his bicycle 32 miles. He swims and rides the same distance each day. How many miles does Rudy swim and ride each day?

Ⓓ Rudy ate 32 apples in one week. This is 17 more apples than his brother ate. How many apples did Rudy's brother eat?

6. Carlos received $50 for his birthday. He bought a camera for $19 and a basketball for $13. About how much money does Carlos have left to spend?

Ⓐ $10   Ⓒ $30

Ⓑ $20   Ⓓ $40

★assessment

1. Camille bought 8 bags of bread. Each bag had 18 slices of bread. She used 76 slices to make sandwiches for a picnic. Which equation can be used to estimate about how many slices of bread Camille has now?

    (A) $(8 \times 18) - 76 = 68$

    (B) $(10 \times 18) - 70 = 110$

    (C) $(8 \times 20) - 80 = 80$

    (D) $(8 \times 10) - 70 = 10$

2. Mrs. Lestage packed 2 bags of sandwiches for a family picnic. Each bag contained 10 sandwiches. Mr. and Mrs. Lestage and their three children shared the sandwiches equally. Which of the following procedures can be used to determine how many sandwiches each person received?

    (A) Find the product of 2 and 10, then add 5 to this number to find a sum of 25.

    (B) Find the difference between 10 and 2, then multiply by 5 to find a product of 40.

    (C) Find the sum of 10 and 2, then subtract 5 to find a difference of 7.

    (D) Find the product of 2 and 10, then divide by 5 to find a quotient of 4.

3. Jill bought a pair of shoes for $36 and a jacket for $43. She paid with a $100 bill. Which of the following could Jill use to estimate about how much change she should receive?

    (A) $100 - 40 + 40$

    (C) $100 - 40 - 40$

    (B) $100 \times 40 + 40$

    (D) $100 - 30 - 40$

4. Which of the following problems could be solved using this equation?

    $$(4 \times 6) \div 3 = \boxed{}$$

    (A) Mr. White has 4 salesmen at his automobile dealership. Each salesman has a goal to sell 6 cars every week. How many cars would the salesmen sell in 3 weeks?

    (B) White's Auto World received 4 trailers of new cars. Each trailer carried 6 cars. Mr. White wants to put the cars into 3 rows on his car lot. How many cars will be in each row?

    (C) White's Auto World received a shipment of new vehicles. There were 4 cars, 6 SUVs, and 3 trucks. How many vehicles did White's Auto World receive?

    (D) White's Auto World received 4 trailers of new cars. Each trailer held 6 cars. Mr. White discovered that 3 of the cars had been damaged in shipment. How many cars were not damaged in shipment?

5. Henry plants 5 flowers every day for 8 days. At the end of 9 days, Henry had planted 42 flowers. Write and solve an equation to find the number of flowers Henry planted on day 9.

    Answer: _____

    Henry paid $1 for each flower he planted. Before he bought all of the flowers, he had earned $46 for allowance and $55 for babysitting. How much money did Henry have left after buying the flowers? Show all work.

    Answer: _____

 Level 3

Analysis/Analyze

1. Kelsey follows a routine after school. First, she completes her homework then watches her favorite television show. After that, she reads a book before going to bed. On Tuesday and Thursday, Kelsey goes to soccer practice. On soccer practice days, she does not watch television. The chart shows how much time Kelsey spends on each activity.

   In one school week, how much more time does Kelsey spend doing homework than watching television after school?

Kelsey's Activities

Activity	Time
Television	35 min
Reading	22 min
Homework	45 min
Soccer	50 min

   Answer: _____

Synthesis/Create

2. Write a word problem that could be solved using this equation: $(72 \div 8) \times 30 = x$.

   _____

   _____

   _____

   _____

   _____

Journal: Evaluation/Evaluate

In your opinion, is it easier to solve a 1-step problem that contains extra information or a 2-step problem that has no extra information? Explain your answer.

_____

_____

_____

_____

_____

Name _____

Number Line Wipe Out

Play *Number Line Wipe Out* with a partner. Players need two 1-6 number cubes or dot cubes, a pencil, and a paper clip (or hair pin) for the spinner. Each player uses his/her own game sheet. In turn, each player spins the spinner and rolls the number cubes, resulting in 3 one-digit numbers. The player must use all three numbers and any combination of operations (addition, subtraction, multiplication, or division) that will result in a whole number answer between 1 and 30. The player marks a dot on that answer on his/her number line. If the answer has already been marked, the player loses that turn. The player with the most numbers "wiped out" on the number line when the teacher calls time is the winner.

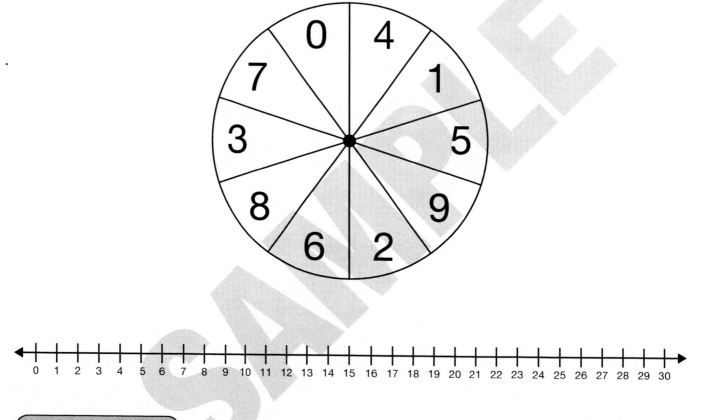

Parent Activities

1. Use a set of dominoes turned face down. Have your child select a domino and state the number shown on each half of the domino. Roll a number cube (die) to generate a third number. Have your child use the four operations (addition, subtraction, multiplication, and division) to solve a problem using these numbers.

2. Plan a grocery store trip. Give your child a list of 3 to 5 items to purchase and a specified amount of money to spend. Have your child estimate the total cost of the items as well as how much change he/she should receive at the check-out counter.

3. Remove face cards from a deck of playing cards and shuffle the remaining cards. Have your child turn over the top three cards to represent three 1-digit numbers. Have your child use the 3 numbers in any order to perform a combination of operations. For example, if your child turns over 3, 4, and 8, you might ask your child to find the sum of 3 and 4, then multiply that number by 8.

 Level 3

Name _____

1. Eli and Daniel are brothers. They made a table showing their ages during several different years.

Brothers' Ages

Eli's Age (years)	Daniel's Age (years)
11	3
13	5
15	7

Describe the pattern you see between Eli's age and Daniel's age.

_____

_____

How old will Eli be when Daniel is 19?

Answer: _____

2. Leslie bought a bag of 100 chocolate candies. She ate 4 candies per day until she had only 76 candies left. Leslie used a hundred chart to show how many days she ate candy. Show how you think Leslie marked her hundred chart.

1	2	3	4	5	6	7	8	9	10
11	12	13	14	15	16	17	18	19	20
21	22	23	24	25	26	27	28	29	30
31	32	33	34	35	36	37	38	39	40
41	42	43	44	45	46	47	48	49	50
51	52	53	54	55	56	57	58	59	60
61	62	63	64	65	66	67	68	69	70
71	72	73	74	75	76	77	78	79	80
81	82	83	84	85	86	87	88	89	90
91	92	93	94	95	96	97	98	99	100

How many days did Leslie eat candy? _____

Explain your answer. _____

_____

3. Samuel is preparing to run a marathon. He increases his running distance each week as shown on this table.

Samuel's Running Distance

Week	Distance (mi)
1	4
2	8
3	12
4	16

Describe the pattern you see between the week number and the distance Samuel runs.

_____

_____

Samuel continues the pattern. How many miles will he run in week 7?

Answer: _____

4. Joe shaded a column on a multiplication table.

Multiplication Table

X	1	2	3	4	5	6	7	8	9
1	1	2	3	4	5	6	7	8	9
2	2	4	6	8	10	12	14	16	18
3	3	6	9	12	15	18	21	24	27
4	4	8	12	16	20	24	28	32	36
5	5	10	15	20	25	30	35	40	45
6	6	12	18	24	30	36	42	48	54
7	7	14	21	28	35	42	49	56	63
8	8	16	24	32	40	48	56	64	72
9	9	18	27	36	45	54	63	72	81

Write a rule that describes the pattern in the shaded column. _____

_____

Use your pencil to shade another place on the table where you see this same pattern.

Words for the Wise

addend	factor	pattern	sum
chart	multiple	product	table
even number	odd number	rule	

The road to success starts here!

Name _____

1. Chun Ye placed counters on his hundred chart to create a pattern.

1	●	3	●	5	6	7	●	9	10
11	●	13	14	15	●	17	18	19	●
21	22	23	●	25	26	27	●	29	30
31	32	33	34	35	36	37	38	39	40
41	42	43	44	45	46	47	48	49	50

Which statement is **not** true about Chun Ye's pattern?

Ⓐ The next number in the pattern is 32.

Ⓑ All the numbers in the pattern are even.

Ⓒ The rule for the pattern is "Add 4."

Ⓓ The rule for the pattern is "Add 3."

2. All the packages of marshmallows in the snack shop have the same number of marshmallows. The table shows the numbers of packages and the numbers of marshmallows.

Marshmallow Packages

Number of Packages	Number of Marshmallows
2	16
3	24
4	32

How many marshmallows are in 6 packages?

Ⓐ 48   Ⓒ 34

Ⓑ 40   Ⓓ 33

3. Use the multiplication table to identify patterns.

Multiplication Table

X	1	2	3	4	5	6	7	8	9
1	1	2	3	4	5	6	7	8	9
2	2	4	6	8	10	12	14	16	18
3	3	6	9	12	15	18	21	24	27
4	4	8	12	16	20	24	28	32	36
5	5	10	15	20	25	30	35	40	45
6	6	12	18	24	30	36	42	48	54
7	7	14	21	28	35	42	49	56	63
8	8	16	24	32	40	48	56	64	72
9	9	18	27	36	45	54	63	72	81

Which statement about whole numbers is true?

Ⓐ The product of 3 and any factor must be an odd number.

Ⓑ The product of 8 and any factor must be an even number.

Ⓒ A multiple of 8 is also a multiple of 6.

Ⓓ Any number that is a multiple of 9 is also a multiple of 6.

4. Shelley's bathroom scale is not working correctly. Shelley had 4 friends weigh on her scale. The table shows their weights on Shelley's scale and their actual weights in pounds (lb.).

Weight Comparison

Shelley's Scale Weight (lb.)	81	104	92	75
Actual Weight (lb.)	64	87	75	58

Shelley's father weighs 187 pounds on her scale. What is his actual weight?

Ⓐ 204 lb.   Ⓒ 180 lb.

Ⓑ 194 lb.   Ⓓ 170 lb.

 Level 3

1. James can buy 2 gumballs for 5¢. He made a table of the numbers of gumballs and their costs.

Gumball Costs

Number of Gumballs	2	4	6	8
Cost	5¢	10¢	15¢	20¢

How many gumballs can James buy for 35¢?

Ⓐ 10   Ⓒ 14

Ⓑ 12   Ⓓ 16

2. Use this addition table to answer the question.

Addition Table

+	1	2	3	4	5	6	7	8	9
1	2	3	4	5	6	7	8	9	10
2	3	4	5	6	7	8	9	10	11
3	4	5	6	7	8	9	10	11	12
4	5	6	7	8	9	10	11	12	13
5	6	7	8	9	10	11	12	13	14
6	7	8	9	10	11	12	13	14	15
7	8	9	10	11	12	13	14	15	16
8	9	10	11	12	13	14	15	16	17
9	10	11	12	13	14	15	16	17	18

Which statement about adding whole numbers is **not** true?

Ⓐ When both addends are the same, the sum is even.

Ⓑ When both addends are the same, the sums form a diagonal.

Ⓒ When both addends are the same, the sums are multiples of 2.

Ⓓ When both addends are the same, the digit in the ones place is either a 2 or a 4.

3. Mrs. Taylor began a new weight-loss program. She hopes to lose 3 pounds every 10 days. This table shows the number of pounds Mrs. Taylor expects to lose for different numbers of days.

Weight Loss

Number of Days	Weight Loss (pounds)
10	3
20	6
30	9
40	12
50	15

Mrs. Taylor would like to lose 30 pounds. Her weight loss continues to follow the pattern shown on the table. How long will it take Mrs. Taylor to lose 30 pounds?

Ⓐ 100 days   Ⓒ 60 days

Ⓑ 90 days   Ⓓ 45 days

4. As Sonia jumped rope, she skip-counted by 6. She noticed a pattern as she counted. Use this multiplication table to find Sonia's pattern.

Multiplication Table

X	1	2	3	4	5	6	7	8	9
1	1	2	3	4	5	6	7	8	9
2	2	4	6	8	10	12	14	16	18
3	3	6	9	12	15	18	21	24	27
4	4	8	12	16	20	24	28	32	36
5	5	10	15	20	25	30	35	40	45
6	6	12	18	24	30	36	42	48	54
7	7	14	21	28	35	42	49	56	63
8	8	16	24	32	40	48	56	64	72
9	9	18	27	36	45	54	63	72	81

What is the pattern Sonia noticed?

Ⓐ The multiples of 6 are also multiples of 3.

Ⓑ The multiples of 6 are also multiples of 4.

Ⓒ The multiples of 6 are also multiples of 5.

Ⓓ The multiples of 6 are also multiples of 8.

Name _____

Use the multiplication table to identify patterns.

Multiplication Table

X	1	2	3	4	5	6	7	8	9
1	1	2	3	4	5	6	7	8	9
2	2	4	6	8	10	12	14	16	18
3	3	6	9	12	15	18	21	24	27
4	4	8	12	16	20	24	28	32	36
5	5	10	15	20	25	30	35	40	45
6	6	12	18	24	30	36	42	48	54
7	7	14	21	28	35	42	49	56	63
8	8	16	24	32	40	48	56	64	72
9	9	18	27	36	45	54	63	72	81

1. Which statement about whole numbers is true?

   Ⓐ A multiple of 5 cannot be even.

   Ⓑ A multiple of 9 is always odd.

   Ⓒ A multiple of 6 cannot be even.

   Ⓓ A multiple of 4 is always even.

2. Mrs. Sudhi made a table to show the number of Crispy Treats she put into different numbers of containers. Each container held the same number of Crispy Treats.

Crispy Treats

Number of Containers	4	6	8	10
Number of Crispy Treats	12	18		

   Which pair of numbers completes the table?

   Ⓐ 21, 30   Ⓒ 24, 36

   Ⓑ 24, 30   Ⓓ 20, 30

Use this addition table to help answer questions 3 and 4.

Addition Table

+	1	2	3	4	5	6	7	8	9
1	2	3	4	5	6	7	8	9	10
2	3	4	5	6	7	8	9	10	11
3	4	5	6	7	8	9	10	11	12
4	5	6	7	8	9	10	11	12	13
5	6	7	8	9	10	11	12	13	14
6	7	8	9	10	11	12	13	14	15
7	8	9	10	11	12	13	14	15	16
8	9	10	11	12	13	14	15	16	17
9	10	11	12	13	14	15	16	17	18

3. Which statement is **not** true?

   Ⓐ The sum of two even numbers is even.

   Ⓑ The sum of two odd numbers is odd.

   Ⓒ The sum of an odd number and an even number is odd.

   Ⓓ The sum of an even number and an odd number is odd.

4. Which statement is correct?

   Ⓐ When two addends have a difference of 1, their sum is even.

   Ⓑ When two addends have a difference of 2, their sum is odd.

   Ⓒ When two addends have a difference of 2, their sum is even.

   Ⓓ When two addends are the same, their sum is odd.

5. Eloise and Sarah are sisters. They made a table showing their grade levels in school for several different years.

Sisters' Grade Levels in School

Eloise	4	5	8	11
Sarah	1	2	5	8

In what grade was Sarah when Eloise was in the ninth grade? _____

 Level 3

Analysis/Analyze

1. Maggie used toothpicks to make a line of triangles as shown.

   She made the following table to show how many toothpicks she used as she made her design longer.

   Triangles and Toothpicks

Number of Triangles	1	2	3	4
Number of Toothpicks	3	5	7	9

   Maggie wants to extend her toothpick triangle pattern to 8 triangles. How many toothpicks will she use?

   Answer: _____

   What patterns do you see on Maggie's table?

   _____

Analysis/Analyze

2. Jody cut a blank hundred chart along the lines to create puzzle-shaped pieces. He wrote a number in one of the squares. Use what you know about the hundred chart and place value to find the missing numbers in this piece.

   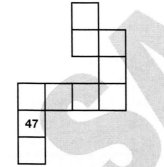

   Explain how you found your answers.

   _____

   _____

   _____

   _____

Journal: Analysis/Analyze

The product of two even factors is always even. The product of two odd factors is always odd. Write a generalization about the product of an even factor and an odd factor. Give examples to support your generalization.

_____

_____

_____

_____

Name _____

Math Rules!

Play *Math Rules!* in groups of 3-4 students. Each group needs a ten-sided die or a 1-10 spinner. At the beginning of play, one student in each group is selected to be the "Function Machine." The function machine selects a secret rule such as: × 7, + 9, − 6, etc. In turn, other players roll the die or spin the spinner to generate an input number. The player says the input number aloud, and the function machine silently applies the secret rule, calling the output number aloud. All players record both numbers on one of the tables below. The next player then rolls or spins a number, and the function machine applies the same secret rule to give the related output number. Again, both numbers are recorded below the first pair of related numbers by all students in the group. Play continues until a player correctly guesses the secret rule.

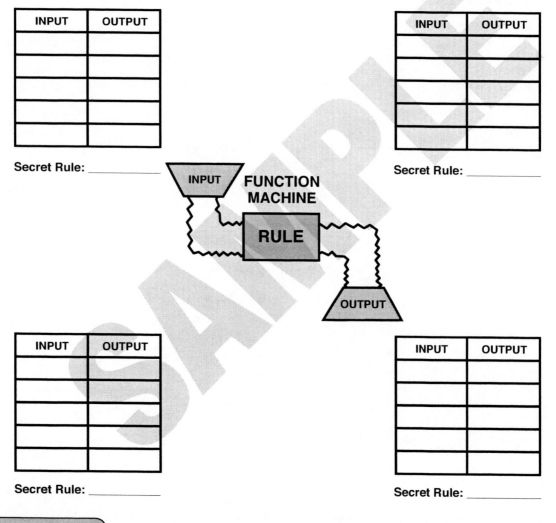

INPUT	OUTPUT

Secret Rule: _____

INPUT	OUTPUT

Secret Rule: _____

INPUT	OUTPUT

Secret Rule: _____

INPUT	OUTPUT

Secret Rule: _____

Parent Activities

1. Discuss things that come in 3s (e.g., 3 sides on a triangle, 3 legs on a tripod, 3 strikes, 3 feet in 1 yard, etc.). Skip count by 3, and record the numbers, noting if they are even or odd. Repeat this activity with different numbers.

2. Using toy cars, discuss how many wheels are on 1 car. Then have your child find how many wheels are on 2 cars, 3 cars, etc. Make a table showing the data.

3. Ask your child how many dimes are in $1, $2, $5, etc.

 Level 3

1. On Tuesday, Mr. Sokol drove his truck 748 miles. Rounded to the nearest hundred, what is the best estimate of the number of miles Mr. Sokol drove on Tuesday?

   Answer: _____

2. When Tina awoke, the outside temperature was 72°F. The temperature that night was 88°F. She rounded both temperatures to the nearest ten and found the difference. What equation did Tina use?

   Answer: _____

3. Jasmine told her mother that there were about 50 students in her P.E. class. She rounded the actual number of students to the nearest 10. What is the greatest number of students that could be in Jasmine's P.E. class?

   Answer: _____

   What is the smallest number of students that could be in Jasmine's P.E. class?

   Answer: _____

4. Derris is writing a report about the number of kilowatt hours of electricity his family used last month. According to the monthly electric bill, his family used 857 kilowatt hours last month. Derris rounds that number to the nearest 10. What number will he use in his report?

   Answer: _____

5. The chart shows the numbers of different fish Dorothy has in her aquarium.

   ### Dorothy's Fish

Type of Fish	Number of Fish
Tetra	14
Molly	36
Guppy	23
Neon	25

   Write an equation that shows how to estimate the number of fish in Dorothy's aquarium.

   Answer: _____

6. Phillip has 321 baseball cards and 249 football cards. Write an equation that shows one way to estimate, to the nearest hundred, how many more baseball cards Phillip has than football cards.

   Answer: _____

Words for the Wise

You've got this down cold!

approximate   digits   estimate   round

partner practice

1. Dante has 643 stamps in his stamp collection. What is this number rounded to the nearest hundred?

Ⓐ 600

Ⓑ 640

Ⓒ 650

Ⓓ 700

2. Carol has 56 dolls in her collection. She rounds this number to the nearest 10. About how many dolls are in Carol's collection?

Ⓐ 50

Ⓑ 55

Ⓒ 60

Ⓓ 65

3. Look at these two groups of numbers.

Group X	Group Y
85	297
88	304
93	299

Which statement about the numbers in these groups is true?

Ⓐ When rounding to the nearest ten, all numbers in Group X round to 80.

Ⓑ When rounding to the nearest hundred, all numbers in Group Y round to 290.

Ⓒ When rounding to the nearest ten, all numbers in Group X round to 100.

Ⓓ When rounding to the nearest hundred, all numbers in Group Y round to 300.

4. Last year, 3441 tropical fish were sold at The Fish Tank. What is this number rounded to the nearest hundred?

Ⓐ 3000

Ⓑ 3400

Ⓒ 3440

Ⓓ 3500

5. Montel told a news reporter that about 780 students attend his school. Montel rounded the actual number of students at his school to the nearest 10. Which of the following is the greatest number of students that could attend his school?

Ⓐ 774   Ⓒ 786

Ⓑ 784   Ⓓ 789

6. The chart shows the number of miles Mr. Parson drove last week.

Mr. Parson's Mileage

Day of Week	Number of Miles
Monday	104
Tuesday	183
Wednesday	279
Thursday	148

Which equation best shows an estimate of how many more miles Mr. Parson drove on Wednesday than Thursday?

Ⓐ 200 + 100 = 300

Ⓑ 200 − 100 = 100

Ⓒ 300 − 100 = 200

Ⓓ 300 − 200 = 100

          Level 3

Name _____

1. Terrell read 468 pages last month. Demetri read 711 pages. Which equation best shows a way to estimate the number of pages Terrell and Demetri read?

   Ⓐ 500 + 700 = 1200

   Ⓑ 700 − 500 = 200

   Ⓒ 400 + 700 = 1100

   Ⓓ 500 + 800 = 1300

2. Arlo has 435 baseball cards. He rounds this number to the nearest 100. About how many baseball cards does Arlo have?

   Ⓐ 500

   Ⓑ 430

   Ⓒ 400

   Ⓓ 350

3. Look at the two groups of numbers.

Group X	Group Y
54	411
51	356
48	407

   Which statement about the numbers in these groups is true?

   Ⓐ When rounding to the nearest ten, all numbers in Group X round to 60.

   Ⓑ When rounding to the nearest hundred, all numbers in Group Y round to 400.

   Ⓒ When rounding to the nearest hundred, all numbers in Group X round to 100.

   Ⓓ When rounding to the nearest ten, all numbers in Group Y round to 410.

4. Gabriella's mother bought a new refrigerator that cost approximately $900. Which of the following was most likely the actual price of the refrigerator?

   Ⓐ $971

   Ⓑ $960

   Ⓒ $895

   Ⓓ $848

5. Tia's father asked her to research the cost of a laptop computer. She found that a new laptop could be purchased for as little as $465. What figure should Tia tell her father if she rounds the price of the laptop to the nearest 10?

   Ⓐ $400   Ⓒ $470

   Ⓑ $460   Ⓓ $500

6. The chart shows the number of each type of ball Coach Paul has in the equipment room.

   Balls in Equipment Room

Type of Ball	Number of Balls
Basketball	22
Soccer ball	34
Football	17
Baseball	46

   Which equation best shows a way to estimate the total number of balls Coach Paul has in the equipment room?

   Ⓐ 20 + 30 + 10 + 40 = 100

   Ⓑ 20 + 30 + 20 + 50 = 120

   Ⓒ 30 + 30 + 10 + 40 = 110

   Ⓓ 20 + 30 + 20 + 40 = 110

★assessment

1. The third-grade students at Paul Revere Elementary collected 2472 pennies for a school project. Rounded to the nearest hundred, how many pennies did the students collect?

   Ⓐ 2000   Ⓒ 2470

   Ⓑ 2400   Ⓓ 2500

2. Randy rounded the number of nails in a box to 300. Which of these numbers could be the actual number of nails in the box?

   Ⓐ 380   Ⓒ 202

   Ⓑ 267   Ⓓ 157

3. Martese has $204 in her savings account. She received $75 for her birthday. Which equation best shows a way to estimate the total amount of money Martese has?

   Ⓐ $200 + 70 = 270$

   Ⓑ $300 + 80 = 380$

   Ⓒ $200 + 80 = 280$

   Ⓓ $200 - 80 = 120$

4. When Ellie talked to her grandmother about her vacation, she told her grandmother that she had traveled about 1200 miles. Ellie rounded the actual miles she traveled to the nearest hundred. Which of the following could be the number of miles she traveled?

   Ⓐ 1125 miles   Ⓒ 1250 miles

   Ⓑ 1177 miles   Ⓓ 1260 miles

5. When rounding to the nearest ten, which of the following numbers will **not** round to 60?

   Ⓐ 55   Ⓒ 63

   Ⓑ 58   Ⓓ 65

6. Preston goes to school 185 days a year. He rounded the number to the nearest 100. About how many days a year does Preston go to school?

   Ⓐ 200   Ⓒ 180

   Ⓑ 190   Ⓓ 100

7. The chart shows the number of each type of cookie Mrs. Montana baked.

   ## Mrs. Montana's Cookies

Type of Cookie	Number of Cookies
Chocolate chip	48
Oatmeal	36
Sugar	24

   Write an equation showing how to use rounding to estimate the total number of cookies Mrs. Montanta baked.

   _____

   Did you choose to round to the nearest 10 or to the nearest 100? _____

   Explain why you made this choice. _____

   _____

 Level 3

Name _____

Application/Apply

1. Steve is rounding three-digit numbers to the nearest hundred.

What is the smallest number he could round to 800?

Answer: _____

What is the largest number Steve could round to 800?

Answer: _____

Analysis/Analyze

2. If rounded to the nearest 10, a mystery number rounds to 350. If rounded to the nearest 100, the mystery number rounds to 400.

What is the smallest number that could be the mystery number?

Answer: _____

What is the largest number that could be the mystery number?

Answer: _____

Journal: Application/Apply

Explain a situation in everyday life where you use rounding to estimate.

_____

_____

_____

_____

_____

★ motivation station

Roll and Round

Play *Roll and Round* with a partner or in a small group. In turn, each player rolls 3 dice and records the numbers in the **"Digits Rolled"** column of the table below. The player decides what number to create using the 3 digits and records this number in the **"My Number"** column. The player then spins the spinner to determine whether to round the number to the nearest 10 or 100 and records the rounded number in the **"Rounded Number"** column. On each play, the player adds the new rounded number to the previous rounded number and keeps a running total. The object of the game is to be the first player closest to the target number of 1000 without going over. A player may choose to stop rolling at any point in the game if he/she believes that continuing play would exceed the target number of 1000.

Spinner	Digits Rolled	My Number	Rounded Number
100 10 10 100 100 10			
	Target Number		**1000**

Parent Activities

1. Model rounding numbers. When you fill your car with gasoline, make comments to your child such as, "It took 19 gallons of gas to fill my car. That is almost 20 gallons. It cost $48 to fill the car. That is almost $50."

2. Talk with your child about how you use rounding in your daily life (e.g., to estimate the cost of something, to figure about how much of something you need).

 Level 3

1. Austin has 213 red paper clips, 508 blue paper clips, and 334 green paper clips. He is making a chain using all the red and blue paper clips. How many paper clips will Austin use to make his chain?

Answer: _____

2. Study this number line.

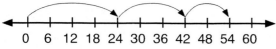

Write the equation that is represented by this number line.

Answer: _____

3. Carey, Jack, and Evan collect baseball cards. Carey has 805 cards. Carey has 187 more cards than Jack, and Evan has 365 more cards than Jack.

How many baseball cards does Jack have? How did you find this number?

Answer: _____

_____

How many baseball cards does Evan have? How did you find this number?

Answer: _____

_____

4. Ty solved this problem in math.

$$\begin{array}{r} 257 \\ + 374 \\ \hline 631 \end{array}$$

How could Ty prove that his answer is correct?

Answer: _____

_____

5. Albert wrote these number pairs according to a rule.

534, 803   145, 414   208, 477

What rule did Albert use?

Answer: _____

Write another number pair that fits the rule.

Answer: _____

6. Gerald is reading a book that is 251 pages long. He must read 24 more pages to finish the book.

What is the total number of pages Gerald has read so far? Show your work.

Answer: _____

Words for the Wise

addend	decompose	inverse operations	regroup
addition	difference	operation	subtraction
compose	equation	place value	sum

You are brilliant!

partner practice

1. A total of $620 was won by students at the local history fair. Marty won $350. Cindy won $75. Alvin won the rest. Which statement shows one way to find how much Alvin won?

   Ⓐ Add $350 and $75, and then subtract the sum from $620.

   Ⓑ Subtract $350 from $620.

   Ⓒ Add $620, $350, and $75.

   Ⓓ Add $620 and $350, and then subtract $75 from the total.

2. Callie made friendship bracelets to give her best friends on Valentine's Day. She used 216 red beads and 277 pink beads. To find the total number of beads she used, Callie solved this problem.

   $$\begin{array}{r} 216 \\ +\ 277 \\ \hline 493 \end{array}$$

   How could Callie check her work to see if her answer is correct?

   Ⓐ Callie could add 493 and 277.

   Ⓑ Callie could subtract 216 from 277.

   Ⓒ Callie could subtract 277 from 493.

   Ⓓ Callie could add 216 to 493.

3. Adrienne wrote number pairs according to a rule.

   702, 567   365, 230   815, 680

   Which other number pair fits Adrienne's rule?

   Ⓐ 643, 508   Ⓒ 275, 150

   Ⓑ 597, 460   Ⓓ 413, 274

4. August, Rafael, and Orlando collect baseball cards. August has 757 cards in his collection. Rafael has 153 fewer baseball cards than August but 228 more cards than Orlando.

   Which procedure should be followed to determine how many baseball cards Orlando has?

   Ⓐ Find the sum of 757 and 153, then subtract 228.

   Ⓑ Find the difference between 757 and 228, then add 153.

   Ⓒ Find the difference between 757 and 153, then subtract 228.

   Ⓓ Find the sum of 153 and 228, then add 757.

5. The Keenan family had $235 to spend at Six Flags for meals and souvenirs. They paid $56 for lunch and bought souvenirs for $104.

   How much money did the Keenan family have left at the end of the day?

   Ⓐ $395   Ⓒ $135

   Ⓑ $160   Ⓓ $75

6. This chart shows the new books Mrs. Cortez ordered for the school library.

   Library Books

	Fiction	Non-fiction
Fall	114	109
Spring	142	127

   How many more books in all did Mrs. Cortez order in the spring than in the fall?

   Ⓐ 28

   Ⓑ 46

   Ⓒ 223

   Ⓓ 269

         Level 3

1. Joshua, Carson, and Francisco collect marbles. Joshua has 427 marbles. Carson has 165 more marbles than Joshua, and Francisco has 279 fewer marbles than Carson.

   Which of the following lists the boys in order from fewest number of marbles to greatest number of marbles?

   Ⓐ Carson, Francisco, Joshua

   Ⓑ Francisco, Carson, Joshua

   Ⓒ Francisco, Joshua, Carson

   Ⓓ Carson, Joshua, Francisco

2. Mrs. Kern flew 742 miles (mi.) in her helicopter in two days. She flew 378 miles the first day. How many miles did Mrs. Kern fly the second day?

   Ⓐ 1120 miles   Ⓒ 364 miles

   Ⓑ 1106 miles   Ⓓ 362 miles

3. Rashad and his friends had a video game contest. Rashad recorded the number of points they scored on their favorite video game in this chart.

   Video Game Points

Name	Points
Rashad	692
Leon	348
Jack	277

   Which of the following is true about the points in Rashad's chart?

   Ⓐ Leon scored 344 fewer points than Rashad.

   Ⓑ The sum of all points was 1217.

   Ⓒ Rashad scored 57 more points than the combined scores of Leon and Jack.

   Ⓓ Leon scored 61 more points than Jack.

Use this chart to answer questions 4 and 5.

This chart shows how many lunches the Gourmet Tray Cafeteria served in one week.

Lunches Served

Day	Number of Lunches
Monday	762
Tuesday	835
Wednesday	811
Thursday	796
Friday	908

4. How many fewer lunches were served on the first day of the week than on the last day of the week?

   Ⓐ 142   Ⓒ 266

   Ⓑ 146   Ⓓ 1670

5. What is the difference in the total lunches served on Tuesday and Wednesday and the total lunches served on Thursday and Friday?

   Ⓐ 1704   Ⓒ 62

   Ⓑ 1646   Ⓓ 58

6. At the campout, the Girl Scouts used colored beads to make necklaces. They used 656 red beads, 725 purple beads, 710 yellow beads, and 675 green beads. How many more purple beads than red beads did the girls use?

   Ⓐ 106

   Ⓑ 96

   Ⓒ 79

   Ⓓ 69

assessment

1. The zoo has two giant land tortoises named Timmy and Tommy. Timmy is 27 years older than Tommy. The sum of their ages is 337 years. How old are Timmy and Tommy?

   Ⓐ 337 and 310
   Ⓑ 310 and 27
   Ⓒ 195 and 168
   Ⓓ 182 and 155

2. Lucius solved this subtraction problem.

   $$\begin{array}{r} 703 \\ -248 \\ \hline 455 \end{array}$$

   Which equation could Lucius use to prove that his answer is correct?

   Ⓐ $455 + 248 = \Box$
   Ⓑ $703 + 248 = \Box$
   Ⓒ $455 - 248 = \Box$
   Ⓓ $248 - 455 = \Box$

3. Cedric wrote these number pairs according to a rule.

   50, 13   85, 48   104, 67

   Which other number pair fits Cedric's rule?

   Ⓐ 95, 56
   Ⓑ 115, 78
   Ⓒ 72, 45
   Ⓓ 41, 12

4. Mr. Peña sells different types of birds. In July, he had 3 types of birds for sale.

   Birds for Sale in July

Canaries	14
Parrots	7
Parakeets	33

   Which equation can be used to find how many more parakeets than parrots Mr. Peña had for sale?

   Ⓐ $33 + 14 = \Box$
   Ⓒ $33 - \Box = 14$
   Ⓑ $7 + \Box = 33$
   Ⓓ $33 + 7 = \Box$

5. The Raiders' soccer team raised money for equipment. Kelly collected $250 and Hunter collected $190 for the team. They spent $99 on new soccer balls and $132 on new jerseys. Which shows a way to find the amount of money the soccer team has left?

   Ⓐ Add $250 and $190. Subtract $99, then add $132.

   Ⓑ Add $250 and $190. Add $99, then subtract $132.

   Ⓒ Subtract $190 from $250. Subtract $99, then subtract $132.

   Ⓓ Add $250 and $190. Subtract $99, then subtract $132.

6. Janet, Lamesha, Diane, and Arlene baked cookies for the school carnival. Lamesha baked a dozen less cookies than Diane. Diane baked 26 more cookies than Arlene. Janet baked 37 more cookies than Lamesha. Arlene baked 84 cookies. The girls placed all their cookies on the bake sale table. How many cookies did the girls place on the table?

   Answer: _____

   Which girl baked the greatest number of cookies?

   Answer: _____

Level 3

Analysis/Analyze

1. Margot thought of a mystery number. She added 104 to her number and then subtracted 67 from the sum to get an answer of 423. What was Margot's mystery number?

Answer: _____

Explain how you found your answer.

_____

_____

Analysis/Analyze

2. In a recent election for sheriff, the citizens of Keystone County cast their votes for one of four candidates. The votes are shown on this table.

Keystone County Voting

Candidate	Number of Votes
John Q. Smith	755
Leon Jefferson	874
Emily Lundy	869
Thomas Whitten	509

Emily Lundy asked for a recount, and 58 additional ballots were discovered. Of these 58 ballots, 27 were votes for Emily, 15 were votes for John Smith, and the remaining votes were for Leon Jefferson. What is the total number of votes Leon Jefferson received after the recount?

Answer: _____

Which candidate won the election? Show your work.

Answer: _____

Journal: Analysis/Analyze

Years ago, the terms "carry" and "borrow" were used in mathematics when numbers needed to be composed or decomposed. Why are these terms not accurate?

_____

_____

_____

_____

_____

Up and Down the Mountain

Play *Up and Down the Mountain* with a partner. Each pair of students needs 3 number cubes. Players use individual game boards. In turn, players roll the dice and use the 3 numbers shown to create a 3-digit number. Players repeat to form a second 3-digit number. Players may add or subtract the two numbers they create. The first problem is recorded and solved in box 1. Play passes to player 2 who follows the same procedure on his/her game board. As players climb up the mountain, each sum or difference must be larger than the sum or difference in the preceding box. As players climb down the mountain, each sum or difference must be smaller than the sum or difference in the preceding box. During play, if a player cannot arrive at a sum or difference that is larger or smaller, as needed, the player loses that turn. The first player to successfully climb up and down the mountain is the winner.

Describe a strategy you used when playing the game.

_____

_____

_____

Parent Activities

1. Purchase or make flash cards. Review addition and subtraction facts regularly with your child.

2. Using a box of alphabet cereal, have your child sort a handful of the letters by vowels and consonants. Subtract to see how many more consonants there are than vowels.

3. While traveling, have your child record the numbers on automobile license plates. Use the numbers to practice addition and/or subtraction.

Name _____

1. Mr. Speight's students are divided into 6 groups. Each group built a model with base 10 blocks to show that 5 tens equals 50.

5 tens = 50

All 6 groups put their models together. What is the value of the combined blocks?

Answer: _____

2. Mrs. Smith bought 5 pencils for each of her students. She has 20 students in her class. How many pencils did Mrs. Smith buy?

Answer: _____

3. The manager at the grocery store ordered 9 cartons of canned beans. Each carton contains 30 cans. How many cans of beans did the manager order?

Answer: _____

4. Maggie purchased beads to make bracelets. She purchased 8 bags of beads and paid $6 per bag. Each bag contained 80 beads. How many total beads did Maggie purchase?

Answer: _____

5. Anthony made cookies as gifts for his friends. He decorated 4 boxes and put 60 cookies in each box. How many cookies did Anthony put in his gift boxes?

Answer: _____

6. The Party Factory sells a bouquet of 8 balloons for $7. On Saturday, the Party Factory sold 40 bouquets of balloons. On Sunday, they sold 20 bouquets of balloons. How much money did the Party Factory make over the weekend?

Answer: _____

Explain how you found your answer.

_____

_____

Words for the Wise

factor   multiple   product

Three cheers for math!

★ partner practice

1. Tyreke placed 6 tens on his desk to show the value of 60.

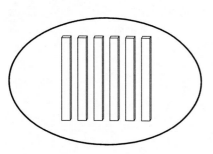

Tyreke drew this model three times in his journal. What would be the value of his new model?

Ⓐ 18   Ⓒ 180

Ⓑ 63   Ⓓ 360

2. Mrs. Singer, the choir teacher, wants to invite 200 parents to the school end-of-year program. She looked at several different packages of invitations. Which of these should Mrs. Singer select in order to have an invitation for each parent?

Ⓐ 2 packages of 10

Ⓑ 2 packages of 50

Ⓒ 4 packages of 20

Ⓓ 4 packages of 50

3. Smith Elementary PTA sold spring flowers for a fund raiser. Each pot contained 6 flowers. The PTA sold 80 pots. How many flowers were sold in all?

Ⓐ 540   Ⓒ 420

Ⓑ 480   Ⓓ 140

4. Hope received five $50 bills for her birthday. How much money did Hope receive?

Ⓐ $25

Ⓑ $100

Ⓒ $250

Ⓓ $500

5. Jessie baked chocolate chip cookies to sell at the school's bake sale. She put 6 cookies into each sack and charged $3 for a sack. Jessie sold 40 sacks of cookies. How much did Jessie earn from the bake sale?

Ⓐ $18

Ⓑ $120

Ⓒ $240

Ⓓ $360

6. Dusty collects baseball cards. He already owned 28 packs, but his grandparents gave him 2 more packs for his birthday. Each pack contains 8 cards. How many cards does Dusty now own?

Ⓐ 16

Ⓑ 56

Ⓒ 240

Ⓓ 280

          Level 3

1. Which one of the following does **not** represent 90?

Ⓐ

Ⓑ 9 groups of ten

Ⓒ 3 × 30

Ⓓ

2. The average length of a song is 3 minutes (min). Maria downloaded 70 songs. She listened to all her songs. How many minutes did Maria listen to music?

Ⓐ 210 min

Ⓑ 100 min

Ⓒ 73 min

Ⓓ 67 min

3. The Splash Car Wash cleaned 60 cars with 4 tires on each car. How many tires were washed in all?

Ⓐ 64

Ⓑ 200

Ⓒ 240

Ⓓ 280

4. Mrs. Collin's third-grade class set a goal to read at home 20 minutes (min) every day of the week. How many minutes would each student read in a week?

Ⓐ 140 min

Ⓑ 120 min

Ⓒ 60 min

Ⓓ 23 min

5. Office Station sells pencils in packages of 70 pencils for $7. Mrs. Johnson purchased 6 packages of pencils for her office. How many pencils did Mrs. Johnson purchase?

Ⓐ 42

Ⓑ 420

Ⓒ 490

Ⓓ 700

6. Cherry candy is sold in bags containing 80 pieces. Monica bought 7 bags of the candy, and Rob bought 9 bags of the candy. How many more pieces of cherry candy did Rob buy than Monica?

Ⓐ 720

Ⓑ 630

Ⓒ 560

Ⓓ 160

★ assessment

1. Johnny listed four ways to represent 4 × 40. Which of the following ways is **not** correct?

   Ⓐ 4 groups of 4 tens

   Ⓑ 80

   Ⓒ 16 tens

   Ⓓ 160

2. Travis ordered 20 ice cream cups for his birthday party. Each cup of ice cream had 7 sprinkles. How many sprinkles were there altogether?

   Ⓐ 70   Ⓒ 210

   Ⓑ 140   Ⓓ 280

3. Leslie helped her father put roses into vases to sell for Valentine's Day. He wanted 7 roses in each vase. Leslie filled 90 vases with roses. How many roses did Leslie put in vases for her father?

   Ⓐ 630   Ⓒ 490

   Ⓑ 560   Ⓓ 420

4. The Spin-About ride at the fair requires 5 tickets. Sixty children rode the Spin-About on Saturday. How many tickets were collected for the Spin-About on Saturday?

   Ⓐ 12

   Ⓑ 65

   Ⓒ 300

   Ⓓ 350

5. Mrs. Anderson took her class of 29 students to a blueberry farm. Mrs. Anderson and her students each picked 4 pints of blueberries to bring home. How many total pints of blueberries did they all pick?

   Ⓐ 93

   Ⓑ 96

   Ⓒ 116

   Ⓓ 120

6. Frank purchased 5 boxes of paper clips with 80 clips in each box. Cecily purchased 6 boxes of paper clips with 70 clips in each box. How many more paper clips did Cecily purchase than Frank? Show all work.

Answer: _____

Name _____

Analysis/Analyze

1. Use a calculator to complete these multiplication problems.

   $5 \times 10 =$ _____ $5 \times 100 =$ _____

   $16 \times 10 =$ _____ $16 \times 100 =$ _____

   $24 \times 10 =$ _____ $24 \times 100 =$ _____

   $55 \times 10 =$ _____ $55 \times 100 =$ _____

   Using the examples above, write a generalization for multiplying a whole number by 10.

   _____

   Using the examples above, write a generalization for multiplying a whole number by 100.

   _____

Synthesis/Create

2. Create a web showing things that come in tens.

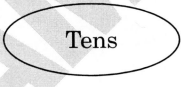

Tens

Journal: Analysis/Analyze

Write in words the steps you use when multiplying 9×60.

_____

_____

_____

_____

_____

Name ____________________________________

Product Path

Play *Product Path* with a partner. Each player needs a game token. Each pair of players needs a number/dot cube and the game board. Players place their game tokens in the START square. In turn, each player rolls the number cube and moves forward the number of spaces shown on the cube. The player multiplies the number in the game-board square by the number rolled. If players find the correct product, they remain on that square until their next turn. If players do NOT find the correct product, they return to their previous square. The winner is the first person to roll past the FINISH square.

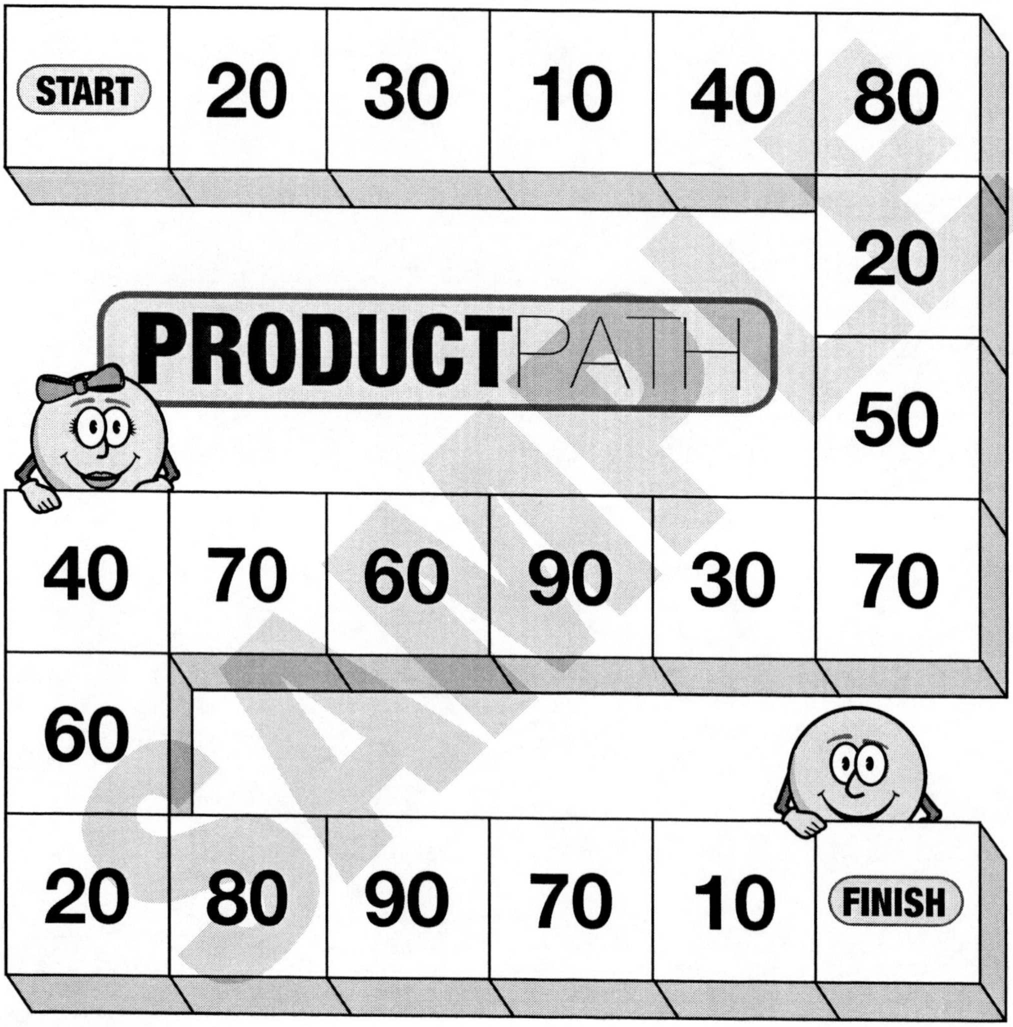
START
20
30
10
40
80
20
50
PRODUCT PATH
40
70
60
90
30
70
60
20
80
90
70
10
FINISH

Parent Activities

1. Practice skip counting by 10s: 10, 20, 30, . . . 100 (both forward and backward).
2. Organize dimes from the family piggy bank into equal stacks and ask your child the value of the dimes. For example, 3 stacks of 8 dimes would equal 240 cents or $2.40. Continue this process with different combinations of dimes, and determine the total amount of money. Then, help your child make a plan of what to do with the money.
3. Glue 10 beans on each of several popsicle sticks or tongue depressors. Give your child story problems that would involve groups of 10. For example, "If each soccer team has 20 players, how many players are on 6 teams?" Children would represent the 20 players with two bean sticks. To show 6 teams, they would make 6 groups of 2 bean sticks (e.g., $6 \times 20 = 120$).

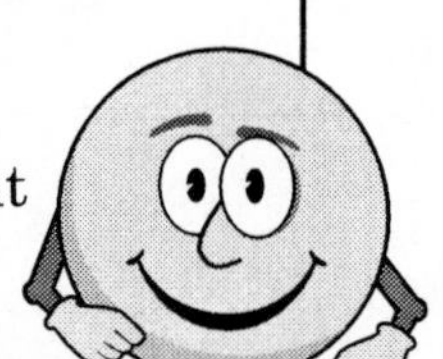

Name _____

1. This rectangle shows $\frac{1}{6}$ of its area shaded. Explain what the fraction $\frac{1}{6}$ represents.

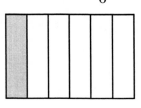

_____

_____

2. Look at this set of doors.

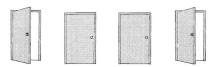

What fraction of the doors are closed?

Answer: _____

What fraction of the doors are open?

Answer: _____

3. Renee has 6 hair bows. Two-sixths of Renee's hair bows are green, $\frac{1}{6}$ of the bows are blue, and $\frac{3}{6}$ of her bows are red. Color the bows to show Renee's hair bows.

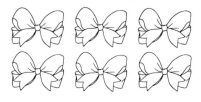

4. Allie ordered a pizza for herself and 2 friends. Each person ate 2 pieces of pizza. Shade the pizza to show how much pizza Allie and her friends ate.

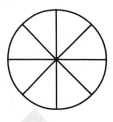

Write the fraction that names the shaded part of the pizza.

Answer: _____

Write the fraction that names the part of the pizza that is left.

Answer: _____

5. Daniel wants to show the fraction $\frac{1}{3}$. He shaded this triangle to show $\frac{1}{3}$.

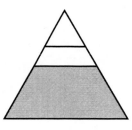

Is Daniel's triangle correctly shaded? How do you know?

_____

_____

Words for the Wise

Nothing can stop you now!

denominator	fourth	half/halves	sixth
eighth	fraction	numerator	third
equal parts	fraction bar	partition	whole

partner practice

Use the diagram to answer questions 1 and 2.

Misha noticed that the four pies in the bakery display case were each cut differently. This picture shows the pies Misha saw.

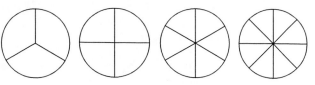

1. Which pie should Misha buy if she wants the largest size pieces?

   Ⓐ the pie cut into thirds

   Ⓑ the pie cut into fourths

   Ⓒ the pie cut into sixths

   Ⓓ the pie cut into eighths

2. Which pie should Misha buy if she wants the greatest number of pieces?

   Ⓐ the pie cut into thirds

   Ⓑ the pie cut into fourths

   Ⓒ the pie cut into sixths

   Ⓓ the pie cut into eighths

3. Keto has a bag that contains 2 red jelly beans, 2 blue jelly beans, and 4 green jelly beans. What fractional part of the jelly beans are green?

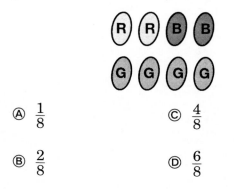

   Ⓐ $\frac{1}{8}$ Ⓒ $\frac{4}{8}$

   Ⓑ $\frac{2}{8}$ Ⓓ $\frac{6}{8}$

4. Which fraction names the shaded part of this figure?

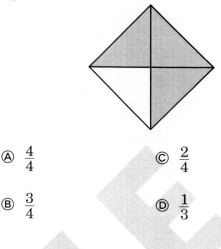

   Ⓐ $\frac{4}{4}$ Ⓒ $\frac{2}{4}$

   Ⓑ $\frac{3}{4}$ Ⓓ $\frac{1}{3}$

5. Look at these figures. Which figure does **not** show $\frac{5}{8}$ shaded?

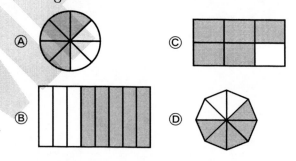

6. Mr. Jones bought ice cream cones for his 6 grandchildren. Some of the children wanted chocolate ice cream and the rest wanted vanilla as shown in this picture.

   What fraction of the ice cream cones were **not** chocolate?

   Ⓐ $\frac{2}{6}$ Ⓒ $\frac{4}{6}$

   Ⓑ $\frac{3}{6}$ Ⓓ $\frac{5}{6}$

Name _____

1. Leanza colored a snowman picture in school. She colored $\frac{1}{2}$ of the snowman's buttons black. Which of these could be Leanza's snowman picture?

2. Which set has $\frac{3}{8}$ of the triangles circled?

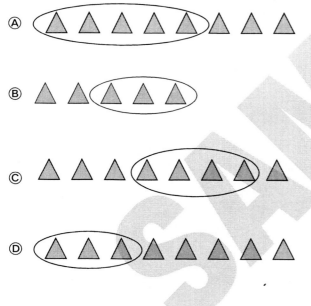

3. What fraction of the figure is **not** shaded?

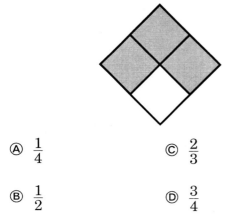

Ⓐ $\frac{1}{4}$　　　Ⓒ $\frac{2}{3}$

Ⓑ $\frac{1}{2}$　　　Ⓓ $\frac{3}{4}$

4. Caleb's father has 8 ties. Three ties are striped, 1 tie has polka dots, and 4 ties are solid colors.

What fraction of the ties have polka dots?

Ⓐ $\frac{7}{8}$　　　Ⓒ $\frac{3}{8}$

Ⓑ $\frac{4}{8}$　　　Ⓓ $\frac{1}{8}$

5. Which figure shows $\frac{1}{4}$ shaded?

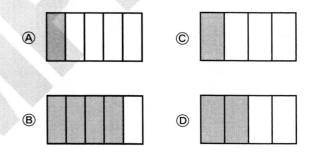

6. Mrs. Ali baked a chicken pie for herself and her son. After the pie was baked, she cut it into 8 equal pieces. Each person ate two pieces. What fraction of the pie was **not** eaten?

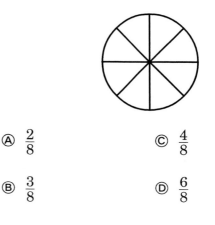

Ⓐ $\frac{2}{8}$　　　Ⓒ $\frac{4}{8}$

Ⓑ $\frac{3}{8}$　　　Ⓓ $\frac{6}{8}$

★ assessment

1. Lisa has three teddy bears on her bed. One of the teddy bears is missing its bow.

   What fraction of the teddy bears does **not** have a bow?

   (A) $\frac{3}{3}$ (C) $\frac{1}{2}$

   (B) $\frac{2}{3}$ (D) $\frac{1}{3}$

2. Dezi designed this flag for a math fair. What fraction of the squares on Dezi's flag do **not** have circles or triangles?

   (A) $\frac{8}{8}$ (C) $\frac{2}{8}$

   (B) $\frac{4}{8}$ (D) $\frac{1}{8}$

3. Which figure shows $\frac{2}{3}$ shaded?

4. Del and his mother went to the bakery. Del noticed some of the brownies were frosted and others were not. Del's mother bought a half-dozen brownies. Four-sixths of the brownies were frosted. Which set shows $\frac{4}{6}$ of the squares shaded?

   (A)

   (B)

   (C)

   (D)

5. What fraction of the pentagons are shaded?

   (A) $\frac{4}{4}$

   (B) $\frac{3}{4}$

   (C) $\frac{2}{4}$

   (D) $\frac{1}{4}$

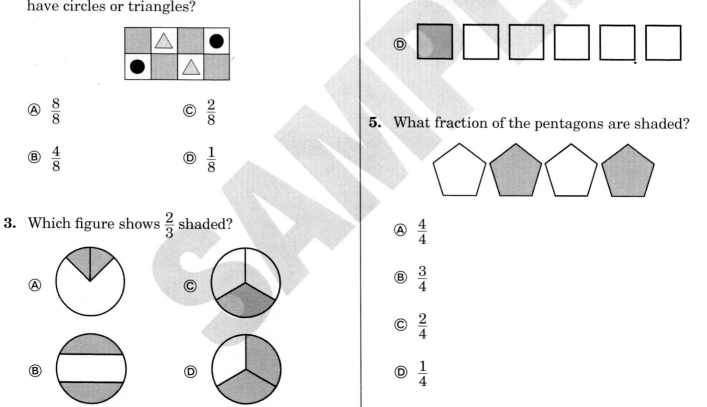

6. Ben folded his paper into 6 equal parts. He colored 2 parts yellow, 3 parts green, and 1 part blue. Write the fraction that shows the part of Ben's paper that is **not** blue.

Y	G	G
Y	G	B

Answer: _____

 Level 3

Analysis/Analyze ————————————————————————————

1. Erika bought a small cake shaped like a rectangle. She planned to cut the cake into 8 equal parts. Draw 3 ways Erika could cut the cake into eighths.

[ ]   [ ]   [ ]

Analysis/Analyze ————————————————————————————

2. Mrs. Bernardy is making ice cream cones for the 6 children at her son's birthday party. One half of the children asked for two scoops, while the other half asked for one scoop. Sketch the ice cream on these cones to show this.

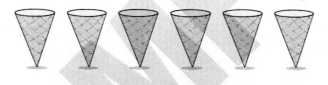

Of the two-scoop ice cream cones, $\frac{1}{3}$ were strawberry. Color the strawberry ice cream. How many ice cream cones were strawberry, two-scoop cones?

Answer: _____

Journal: Application/Apply ————————————————————————

Kaiden ate $\frac{1}{2}$ of this candy bar.   [ ]

Leo ate $\frac{1}{2}$ of this candy bar.   [ ]

Explain why Kaiden ate more candy.

_____

_____

_____

Connect Four Fractions

Play *Connect Four Fractions* with a partner. Each pair of players needs 8 two-color counters, a small cup or plastic container for shaking the counters, a different color crayon for each player, and a game sheet. Player 1 shakes and spills the 8 counters and states the fraction of counters that land red-side up. If the player correctly names the fraction, he/she records the fraction in any circle on the game board and colors the circle. Play then passes to Player 2 and alternates in this manner. The first player to color 4 fraction circles in a row horizontally, vertically, or diagonally is the winner.

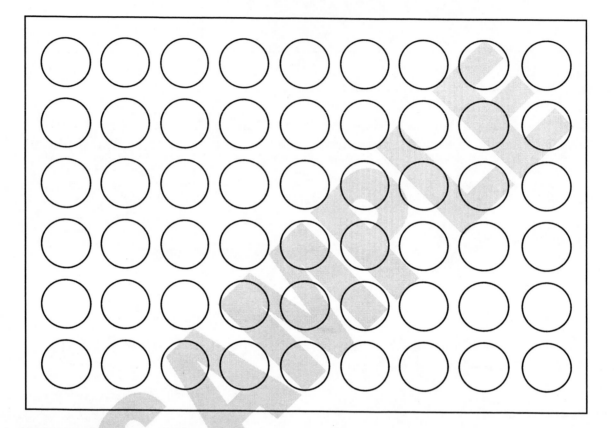

Parent Activities

1. Fractions and food items go hand-in-hand because foods are easily divided into equal parts. Use foods that are already divided or scored (e.g., chocolate bars, graham crackers, pizzas, pies) to show examples of fractions in the real world.

2. Make fraction dominoes. On one end draw a shaded fraction model, and on the other end write a different fraction in numeral form. Make sure that each pictorial fraction model has a matching written fraction on a different domino. Through a process of drawing and matching a fraction model with its correct symbol, the game proceeds until all dominoes have been played.

3. Look for fractional parts of sets. Colors are a great way to generate fractions. For example, tell what fraction of cars in the parking lot are red, what fraction of the candy pieces in the bowl are yellow, what fraction of the flowers in the vase are pink, etc.

4. Build towers with building blocks and name the fractional part for each color or shape (e.g., $\frac{6}{12}$ of the blocks are green or $\frac{3}{12}$ of the blocks are cubes).

Name _____

1. Emma walks to school from her house each day. Emma's school is exactly one mile from her house as shown on this number line. Emma has divided her walk into 4 equally spaced parts.

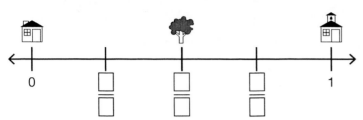

Label each part of Emma's walk with a fraction.

At which fraction along Emma's path is the oak tree located?

Answer: _____

2. A S'mores recipe calls for 1 out of 8 sections of a chocolate bar to be placed on a graham cracker. A number line has been drawn below the chocolate bar.

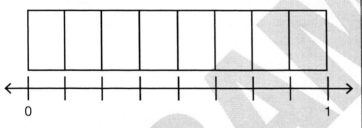

Label the fractions of the whole candy bar on the number line. Then, shade the part needed to make one S'mores.

Which fraction represents the part of the chocolate bar that will be used on a S'mores?

Answer: _____

What fraction of the chocolate bar would be needed to make six S'mores?

Answer: _____

3. On the number line, the line segment between 0 and 1 represents one whole. This whole has been divided into equal segments.

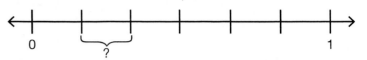

What fraction represents the length of the section labeled with a question mark?

Answer: _____

4. One whole school year is divided equally into 6 grading periods. Adrian drew this number line in the front of his binder to show how much of the school year is left. He moves the star at the end of each grading period.

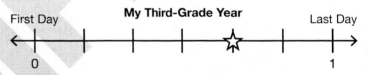

If Adrian places the star on the mark shown above, what fraction of the school year is completed?

Answer: _____

What fraction of the school year remains?

Answer: _____

Explain your answer.

_____

_____

_____

Words for the Wise

denominator	fourth	number line	sixth
eighth	fraction	numerator	third
equal parts	half/halves	partition	

Math matters and you can prove it!

★ **partner practice**

1. Devin wants to show the distance from his house to Lindley Park on a number line. He divides the distance into 3 equal parts. Which of these number lines correctly represents the distance from Devin's house to the park in thirds?

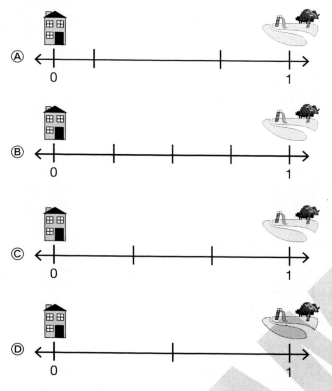

2. Four people were running a 1-mile race. Which runner has completed $\frac{1}{6}$ of the mile as shown on this number line?

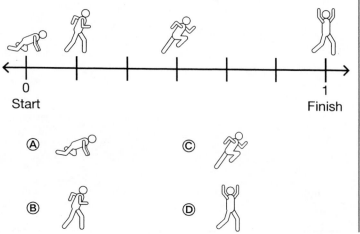

3. On each number line, the distance between 0 and 1 represents one whole. Each whole is divided into equal parts. On which number line does point S represent the fraction $\frac{1}{8}$?

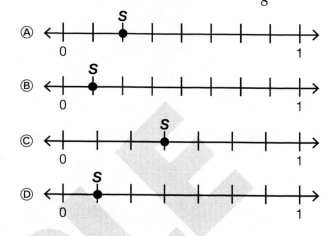

4. On this number line, X marks a point. Which fraction names this point?

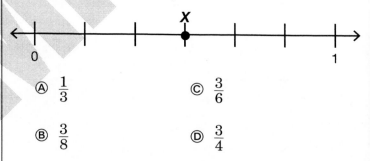

Ⓐ $\frac{1}{3}$ Ⓒ $\frac{3}{6}$

Ⓑ $\frac{3}{8}$ Ⓓ $\frac{3}{4}$

5. On this number line, the segments show how one hour is divided into equal parts. How many minutes (min) would equal $\frac{1}{4}$ hour?

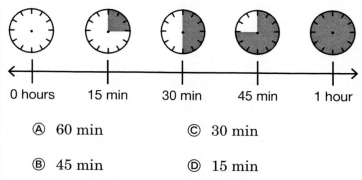

Ⓐ 60 min Ⓒ 30 min

Ⓑ 45 min Ⓓ 15 min

Level 3

1. On each number line, the distance between 0 and 1 represents one whole. Each whole is divided into equal parts. On which number line has the dog run $\frac{1}{6}$ of the way?

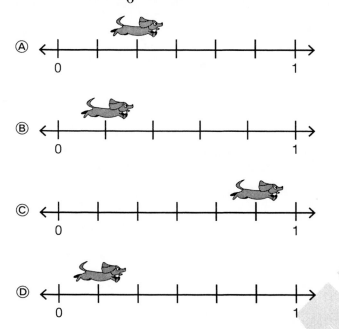

Ⓐ

Ⓑ

Ⓒ

Ⓓ

2. At dog shows, small-breed dogs sit on tables for judging. The drawing shows the set-up for the small-breed judging. The tables are evenly spaced between 0 and 1. Which dog is on the table representing $\frac{2}{3}$ of the distance between 0 and 1?

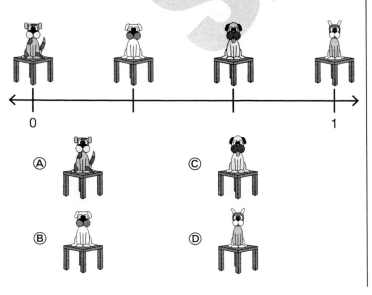

Ⓐ

Ⓑ

Ⓒ

Ⓓ

3. On this number line, the distance between 0 and 1 has been divided into 4 equal parts.

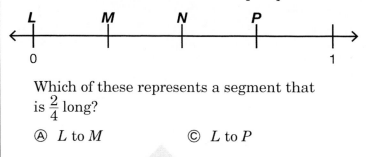

Which of these represents a segment that is $\frac{2}{4}$ long?

Ⓐ L to M Ⓒ L to P

Ⓑ M to N Ⓓ M to P

4. If d represents the number of equal segments between 0 and 1 on the number line, what number would d represent in the labeled fractions?

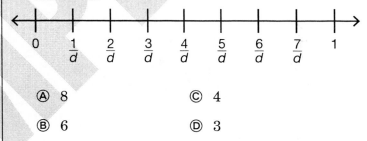

Ⓐ 8   Ⓒ 4

Ⓑ 6   Ⓓ 3

5. Study this number line.

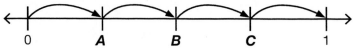

Which statement about the number line is **not** true?

Ⓐ The distance from 0 to 1 on the number line has been divided into 4 equal sections.

Ⓑ The distance between B and C is $\frac{3}{4}$.

Ⓒ Each section on the number line has a length of $\frac{1}{4}$.

Ⓓ The distance from 0 to B can be represented by the fraction $\frac{2}{4}$.

assessment

1. Mrs. Walker gave 4 quarters to her students and explained that this amount equals one whole dollar. She instructed the students to draw a number line diagram in their journals to show how each quarter represents an equal part of the whole dollar. Jamie drew this number line.

$0 $1

What fraction of a dollar is represented by 3 quarters?

Ⓐ $\frac{4}{6}$ Ⓒ $\frac{2}{4}$

Ⓑ $\frac{3}{4}$ Ⓓ $\frac{1}{4}$

2. On these number lines, the distance between 0 and 1 represents one whole. Each whole is divided into eight equal parts. On which number line does point Z represent $\frac{5}{8}$?

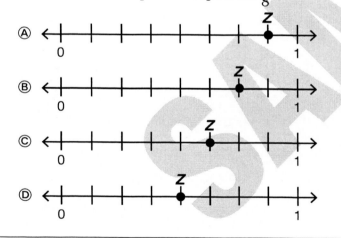

Ⓐ

Ⓑ

Ⓒ

Ⓓ

3. Jake needs to check out a book from the library to finish his science project. It is exactly 1 mile from Jake's house to the library. This map shows the different landmarks spaced out equally between Jake's house and the library.

Jake's House   Library

0 mile   1 mile

Jake leaves his house to walk to the library, but he stops to play on the playground. What fraction of the mile has Jake walked?

Ⓐ $\frac{5}{6}$ Ⓒ $\frac{4}{6}$

Ⓑ $\frac{3}{4}$ Ⓓ $\frac{1}{3}$

4. Jeremy is playing a game with a friend. Each time Jeremy answers a trivia question correctly, he shades one block on his score card.

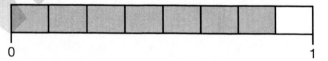

0   1

What fraction of the blocks on the score card does Jeremy have left to shade?

Ⓐ $\frac{1}{8}$ Ⓒ $\frac{6}{8}$

Ⓑ $\frac{3}{8}$ Ⓓ $\frac{7}{8}$

5. This number line has been divided into equal segments. What number should the letter b represent in the fractions that mark the segments on the number line?

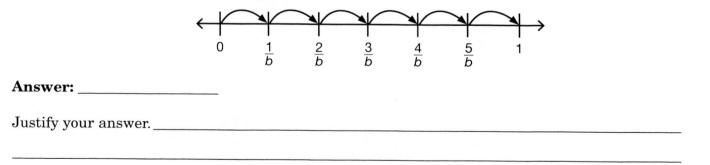

0    $\frac{1}{b}$ $\frac{2}{b}$ $\frac{3}{b}$ $\frac{4}{b}$ $\frac{5}{b}$ 1

Answer: _____

Justify your answer. _____

_____

Name _____

Application/Apply

1. Coach Bradley is planning events for field day. She divided the course into 3 equally spaced sections between the start and the finish. She placed the sack race at the start of the course. The rope pull was located at the end of the course. The balloon race was located $\frac{1}{3}$ of the way from the start. The basketball throw was located between the balloon race and the rope pull. Draw a number line to represent the layout of the field day events. Label your number line with the location of each event as well as the fraction that corresponds to the event.

Analysis/Analyze

2. Lucy wants to use a number line to represent the fraction $\frac{5}{8}$. She drew this number line.

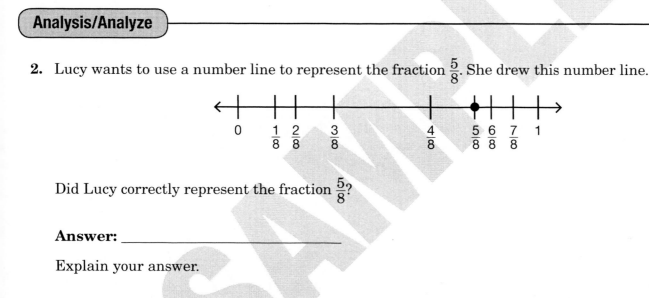

Did Lucy correctly represent the fraction $\frac{5}{8}$?

Answer: _____

Explain your answer.

_____

_____

Journal: Analysis/Analyze

Marco wants to show the fraction $\frac{3}{4}$ on a number line. What are three things Marco must do to correctly represent this fraction?

_____

_____

_____

_____

Name _____

Sock It to Me

Help Mia hang her socks on the correct clothesline. Choose the sock with the correct fraction for each clothesline. Write the fraction on the sock on the clothesline where it belongs.

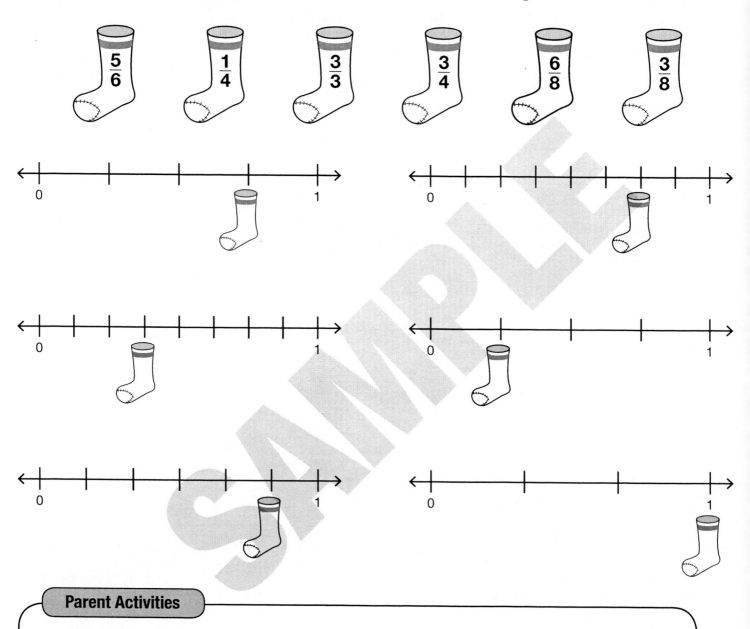

Parent Activities

1. Find objects in your home that are shorter than one inch in length. Using a ruler, help your child determine what fraction each small mark between 0 and 1 represents. Then measure the small objects using fractions of an inch.

2. Draw a number line that is equally divided into 6 parts. Have your child roll a die, use that digit as a numerator, and find the fraction on the number line (e.g., if 4 is rolled, the child locates $\frac{4}{6}$ on the number line).

3. Examine a one-cup measuring cup. Note the vertical scale on the cup may be marked in eighths, fourths, thirds, and halves. Discuss how the scale is similar to a number line.

Name _____

1. Lindy bought a pizza cut into equal pieces. Lindy ate $\frac{1}{2}$ of her pizza. Shade the pizza to show a fraction equivalent to $\frac{1}{2}$.

 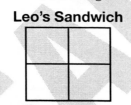

$\frac{1}{2} = \dfrac{\boxed{}}{\boxed{}}$

Using the model, write the fraction that correctly completes the equation.

Franklin ate 4 pieces of Lindy's pizza. Write an equation showing the fraction and whole number representing the part of the pizza eaten by Franklin and Lindy.

Answer: _____

2. Zoe and Leo were each served a peanut butter and jelly sandwich for lunch. Zoe's sandwich was cut into 2 equal parts, and Leo's was cut into 4 equal parts as shown in the diagram.

Zoe's Sandwich   **Leo's Sandwich**

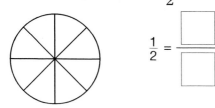

Zoe ate one part of her sandwich, and Leo ate two parts of his sandwich. Leo bragged that he ate more than Zoe. Is this true?

Answer: _____

Why or why not? _____
_____

3. During recycling week, third-grade classes were each given 90-gallon recycling barrels to fill with aluminum cans. The teachers posted number lines showing their students' progress toward filling their class barrels.

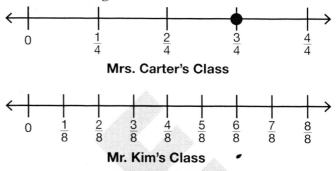

Mrs. Carter's Class

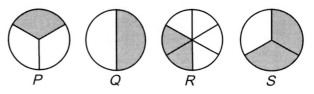

Mr. Kim's Class

Mrs. Carter's class filled $\frac{3}{4}$ of their barrel. Mr. Kim's class has an equal amount of cans. What fraction should be marked on Mr. Kim's number line?

Answer: _____ .

Mrs. Fontana's class filled 1 whole barrel. What fractions on the number lines for Mrs. Carter's class and Mr. Kim's class are equivalent to 1?

Mrs. Carter's Class _____

Mr. Kim's Class _____

4. Look at the shaded parts of the figures.

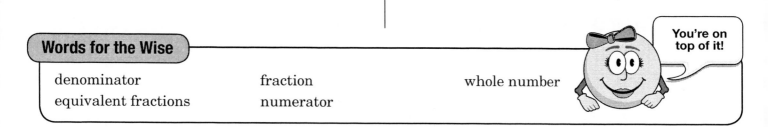

P   Q   R   S

Which 2 figures show equivalent fractions?

Answer: _____

Words for the Wise

denominator	fraction	whole number
equivalent fractions	numerator	

You're on top of it!

★ **partner practice**

Use this chart to answer questions 1 and 2.

Jacie drew a fraction chart to help identify equivalent fractions.

1					
$\frac{1}{2}$			$\frac{1}{2}$		
$\frac{1}{3}$		$\frac{1}{3}$		$\frac{1}{3}$	
$\frac{1}{6}$	$\frac{1}{6}$	$\frac{1}{6}$	$\frac{1}{6}$	$\frac{1}{6}$	$\frac{1}{6}$

1. Which is **not** a correct equation?

   Ⓐ $\frac{3}{6} = \frac{1}{2}$ Ⓒ $\frac{6}{1} = 1$

   Ⓑ $\frac{1}{3} = \frac{2}{6}$ Ⓓ $\frac{4}{6} = \frac{2}{3}$

2. Which fraction is equivalent to 1?

   Ⓐ $\frac{1}{2}$ Ⓒ $\frac{4}{2}$

   Ⓑ $\frac{6}{6}$ Ⓓ $\frac{6}{3}$

3. Joe drew a model of a fraction equivalent to $\frac{6}{8}$. Which model could Joe have drawn?

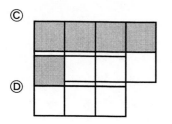

4. Hester has 6 stickers to place on 3 pages. She wants to place the same number of stickers on each page.

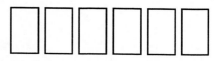

   Which equation shows the number of stickers Hester placed on each page as a fraction and a whole number?

   Ⓐ $\frac{6}{1} = 6$ Ⓒ $\frac{6}{3} = 2$

   Ⓑ $\frac{6}{2} = 3$ Ⓓ $\frac{6}{6} = 1$

5. Which figure does **not** show a fraction that is equivalent to $\frac{1}{2}$?

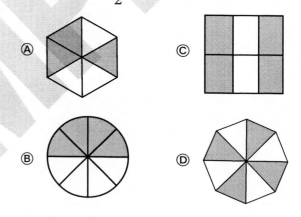

6. Jonathan labeled point P on the number line.

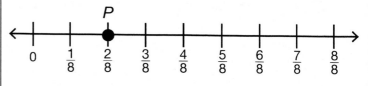

   Which is an equivalent fraction that is also located at point P?

   Ⓐ $\frac{3}{4}$ Ⓒ $\frac{1}{3}$

   Ⓑ $\frac{1}{2}$ Ⓓ $\frac{1}{4}$

     Level 3

Name _____

Use the chart to answer questions 1 – 3.

Kim constructed this fraction chart to find equivalent fractions.

1							
$\frac{1}{2}$				$\frac{1}{2}$			
$\frac{1}{3}$		$\frac{1}{3}$			$\frac{1}{3}$		
$\frac{1}{4}$		$\frac{1}{4}$		$\frac{1}{4}$		$\frac{1}{4}$	
$\frac{1}{6}$	$\frac{1}{6}$	$\frac{1}{6}$	$\frac{1}{6}$	$\frac{1}{6}$	$\frac{1}{6}$		
$\frac{1}{8}$	$\frac{1}{8}$	$\frac{1}{8}$	$\frac{1}{8}$	$\frac{1}{8}$	$\frac{1}{8}$	$\frac{1}{8}$	$\frac{1}{8}$

1. Which shows a pair of equivalent fractions?

   Ⓐ $\frac{1}{2}$ and $\frac{2}{8}$ Ⓒ $\frac{2}{3}$ and $\frac{4}{6}$

   Ⓑ $\frac{3}{8}$ and $\frac{2}{6}$ Ⓓ $\frac{3}{4}$ and $\frac{5}{8}$

2. Which equation is **not** correct?

   Ⓐ $\frac{1}{4} = \frac{2}{8}$

   Ⓑ $\frac{3}{6} = \frac{2}{4}$

   Ⓒ $\frac{6}{8} = \frac{3}{4}$

   Ⓓ $\frac{4}{6} = \frac{5}{8}$

3. Which fraction is equivalent to 1?

   Ⓐ $\frac{3}{3}$ Ⓒ $\frac{2}{3}$

   Ⓑ $\frac{3}{4}$ Ⓓ $\frac{1}{3}$

4. Look at the shaded parts of the figures.

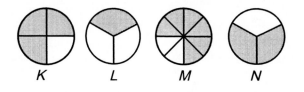

K   L   M   N

   Which 2 figures show equivalent fractions?

   Ⓐ K and L Ⓒ L and N

   Ⓑ K and M Ⓓ K and N

5. Chantell and Tyson are making a quilt. Each created a design for a quilt square as shown.

   Chantell   **Tyson**

   Which equation shows the equivalent fractions represented by the shaded parts of the quilt squares?

   Ⓐ $\frac{2}{2} = \frac{4}{4}$ Ⓒ $\frac{2}{4} = \frac{4}{8}$

   Ⓑ $\frac{2}{6} = \frac{1}{3}$ Ⓓ $\frac{1}{4} = \frac{2}{8}$

6. Griselda baked cinnamon rolls for her family. She cut each cinnamon roll in half and placed the 8 pieces on a platter. Which equation shows a fraction and a whole number representing the total number of cinnamon rolls Griselda baked?

   Ⓐ $\frac{2}{2} = 1$ Ⓒ $\frac{6}{2} = 3$

   Ⓑ $\frac{8}{4} = 2$ Ⓓ $\frac{8}{2} = 4$

★ assessment

Use this chart to answer questions 1 and 2.

Vanessa used fraction tiles to build a fraction chart.

1							
$\frac{1}{2}$				$\frac{1}{2}$			
$\frac{1}{4}$		$\frac{1}{4}$		$\frac{1}{4}$		$\frac{1}{4}$	
$\frac{1}{8}$	$\frac{1}{8}$	$\frac{1}{8}$	$\frac{1}{8}$	$\frac{1}{8}$	$\frac{1}{8}$	$\frac{1}{8}$	$\frac{1}{8}$

1. Which is **not** a correct equation?

   Ⓐ $\frac{1}{4} = \frac{2}{8}$ Ⓒ $\frac{4}{4} = 1$

   Ⓑ $\frac{4}{8} = \frac{1}{2}$ Ⓓ $\frac{3}{4} = \frac{7}{8}$

2. Which is true about a fraction that is equivalent to 1?

   Ⓐ The numerator is greater than the denominator.

   Ⓑ The denominator is greater than the numerator.

   Ⓒ The numerator and the denominator are equal.

   Ⓓ The numerator is less than the denominator.

3. Sylvia has 8 cookies to divide into 2 bags.

   Which equation shows the number of cookies in each bag written as a fraction and a whole number?

   Ⓐ $\frac{2}{8} = \frac{1}{4}$ Ⓒ $\frac{8}{4} = 2$

   Ⓑ $\frac{8}{8} = 1$ Ⓓ $\frac{8}{2} = 4$

4. Jan and Nan ran a marathon. Their friends recorded the girls' progress on these number lines.

   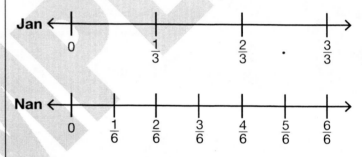

   Jan stopped for water at the rest station when she completed $\frac{2}{3}$ of the marathon. At the same time, Nan stopped at the same station. What fraction on Nan's number line is equivalent to $\frac{2}{3}$?

   Ⓐ $\frac{3}{6}$ Ⓒ $\frac{5}{6}$

   Ⓑ $\frac{4}{6}$ Ⓓ $\frac{6}{6}$

5. Chad and Stephen each ordered a medium pizza. Chad's pizza was cut into 6 equal pieces and Stephen's pizza was cut into 8 equal pieces.

   Chad ate half his pizza. How many pieces did he eat?

   Answer: _____

   Stephen ate half his pizza. How many pieces did he eat?

   Answer: _____

   Complete the equivalent fractions that are shown in this equation.

   $$\frac{1}{2} = \frac{\square}{6} = \frac{\square}{8}$$

Name _____

Analysis/Analyze ──────────────────────────────

1. Use these squares to draw, shade, and label 3 fractions that are equivalent to $\frac{1}{2}$.

☐   ☐   ☐

_____   _____   _____

What patterns do you see in these equivalent fractions?

_____

_____

Analysis/Analyze ──────────────────────────────

2. The Bud Vase Florist is creating a flower arrangement for a customer. The customer wants the arrangement to have yellow, red, and orange carnations. How many red carnations would the florist need to add to the arrangement so that $\frac{1}{2}$ of the arrangement is red?

Answer: _____

Explain why you selected this number.

_____

_____

Journal: Analysis/Analyze ──────────────────────

How can you use an inch ruler to show equivalent fractions?

| 1 in. |

inches   1   2   3

_____

_____

_____

Name _____

Fraction Attraction

Play *Fraction Attraction* with a partner. Each player needs a game board and a pencil and paper clip for the spinner. Player 1 spins the spinner and shades that fraction on the equivalent fraction chart. Play passes to Player 2 who repeats the steps. On each turn as players spin and shade the chart, they identify when equivalent fractions are formed. For example, if a player has shaded $\frac{1}{4}$ and $\frac{2}{8}$, he/she names and records the equivalent fraction pair and scores 1 point. A point can only be claimed on the turn in which the equivalent fraction is first built. The same equivalent fraction cannot be used again by the player, but may be built upon for a later score, e.g., $\frac{1}{2}$ and $\frac{4}{8}$. The first player to score 5 points wins the game.

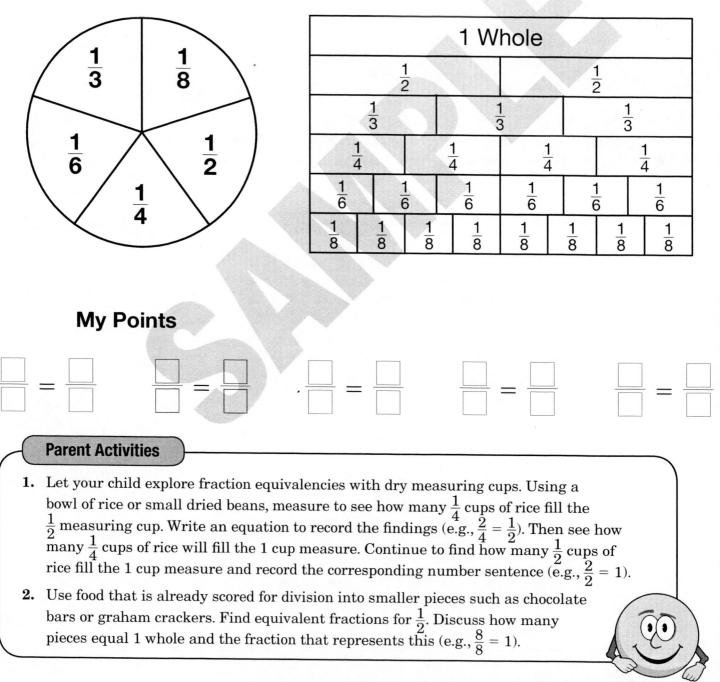

My Points

$\frac{\Box}{\Box} = \frac{\Box}{\Box}$ $\frac{\Box}{\Box} = \frac{\Box}{\Box}$ $\frac{\Box}{\Box} = \frac{\Box}{\Box}$ $\frac{\Box}{\Box} = \frac{\Box}{\Box}$ $\frac{\Box}{\Box} = \frac{\Box}{\Box}$

Parent Activities

1. Let your child explore fraction equivalencies with dry measuring cups. Using a bowl of rice or small dried beans, measure to see how many $\frac{1}{4}$ cups of rice fill the $\frac{1}{2}$ measuring cup. Write an equation to record the findings (e.g., $\frac{2}{4} = \frac{1}{2}$). Then see how many $\frac{1}{4}$ cups of rice will fill the 1 cup measure. Continue to find how many $\frac{1}{2}$ cups of rice fill the 1 cup measure and record the corresponding number sentence (e.g., $\frac{2}{2} = 1$).

2. Use food that is already scored for division into smaller pieces such as chocolate bars or graham crackers. Find equivalent fractions for $\frac{1}{2}$. Discuss how many pieces equal 1 whole and the fraction that represents this (e.g., $\frac{8}{8} = 1$).

Name _____

1. Look at these models.

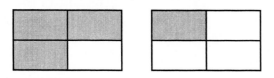

Use fractions to write a number sentence that compares the shaded parts of the two models.

Answer: _____

2. Shade these models to show $\frac{1}{4}$ and $\frac{1}{3}$.

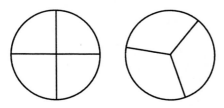

Write a number sentence comparing these two fractions.

Answer: _____

3. Mrs. Moore uses red paper to cover $\frac{3}{8}$ of her bulletin board. She uses blue paper to cover $\frac{5}{8}$ of her bulletin board. Which color of paper covers the largest area of the bulletin board?

Answer: _____

Explain your answer.

_____

4. Shade this model so that less than $\frac{3}{6}$ of the triangles are shaded.

△ △ △ △ △ △

Write the fraction that represents the part of the triangles you shaded.

Answer: _____

What is another fraction that is less than $\frac{3}{6}$?

Answer: _____

5. A survey shows that $\frac{2}{3}$ of the students at Keller Elementary School play a sport after school. The survey also shows that $\frac{2}{6}$ of the students participate in choir. Draw models of these two fractions.

Write a number sentence using >, <, or = to compare the two fractions.

Answer: _____

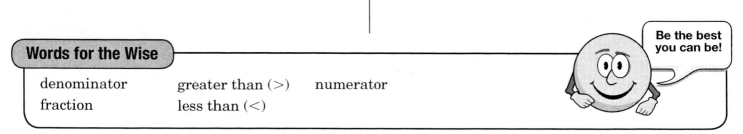

Words for the Wise

| denominator | greater than (>) | numerator |
| fraction | less than (<) | |

Be the best you can be!

partner practice

1. Mrs. Bradshaw measured the heights of her two sons, Ray and Ed. She was surprised to see that Ray had grown $\frac{7}{8}$ inch and Ed had grown $\frac{5}{8}$ inch in three months.

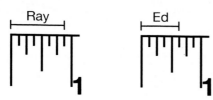

Which number sentence correctly compares how much the boys had grown?

Ⓐ $\frac{7}{8} < \frac{5}{8}$　　　Ⓒ $\frac{5}{8} > \frac{7}{8}$

Ⓑ $\frac{7}{8} = \frac{5}{8}$　　　Ⓓ $\frac{7}{8} > \frac{5}{8}$

2. Mrs. Jefferson uses $\frac{3}{4}$ cup brown sugar when she makes chocolate chip cookies. She uses $\frac{2}{4}$ cup brown sugar when making snickerdoodles.

The models show that —

Ⓐ $\frac{3}{4} = \frac{2}{4}$　　　Ⓒ $\frac{3}{4} > \frac{2}{4}$

Ⓑ $\frac{2}{4} > \frac{3}{4}$　　　Ⓓ $\frac{3}{4} < \frac{2}{4}$

3. Russell compared fractions using the symbols $<, >,$ and $=$. All his statements are correct except one. Which statement is **not** true?

Ⓐ $\frac{3}{8} = \frac{3}{4}$　　　Ⓒ $\frac{2}{6} > \frac{1}{6}$

Ⓑ $\frac{3}{4} > \frac{2}{4}$　　　Ⓓ $\frac{1}{3} < \frac{1}{2}$

4. The hotel chef studied the breakfast buffet to determine which flavor of muffin the customers liked best. She compared the fractions of the muffins eaten as shown in this figure.

Based on the fraction models, which conclusion could the chef make about the muffins eaten?

Ⓐ More customers preferred cranberry muffins because $\frac{4}{8} > \frac{6}{8}$.

Ⓑ An equal number of customers like blueberry muffins and cranberry muffins because $\frac{2}{8} = \frac{4}{8}$.

Ⓒ More customers preferred blueberry muffins because $\frac{6}{8} > \frac{4}{8}$.

Ⓓ Fewer customers preferred blueberry muffins because $\frac{6}{8} < \frac{4}{8}$.

5. Mrs. Jones displayed a fraction chart on her classroom wall.

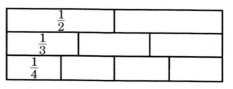

Which of the following number sentences is **not** true?

Ⓐ $\frac{1}{2} > \frac{1}{4}$　　　Ⓒ $\frac{1}{3} < \frac{1}{2}$

Ⓑ $\frac{1}{4} < \frac{1}{3}$　　　Ⓓ $\frac{1}{4} > \frac{1}{2}$

 Level 3

1. Lola cut 8 shapes from paper. She cut more than $\frac{5}{8}$ of the shapes from colored paper. Which group shows more than $\frac{5}{8}$ of the shapes cut from colored paper?

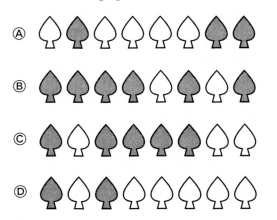

4. Arlo baked three cakes. Each cake was the same size. He cut the first cake into 8 equal pieces, the second cake into 6 equal pieces, and the third cake into 8 equal pieces as shown in this diagram. The shaded parts represent the number of pieces that were eaten.

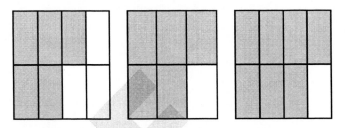

Which number sentence about the shaded parts of the diagram is true?

Ⓐ $\frac{5}{6} = \frac{5}{8}$ Ⓒ $\frac{5}{8} < \frac{5}{6}$

Ⓑ $\frac{5}{8} > \frac{7}{8}$ Ⓓ $\frac{7}{8} < \frac{5}{8}$

2. Jackie, Erica, and Zana each ordered a small pizza. Jackie ate $\frac{3}{6}$ of her pizza. Erica ate $\frac{3}{8}$ of her pizza, and Zana ate $\frac{3}{4}$ of her pizza. Which statement is true?

Ⓐ Jackie ate more pizza than Zana.

Ⓑ Zana ate less pizza than Erica.

Ⓒ The three girls all ate equal amounts of pizza.

Ⓓ Erica ate less pizza than Jackie.

5. A truck and a car are traveling from the park to the store. The distance between the park and the store is one mile.

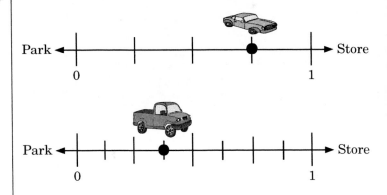

Which number sentence below correctly compares the distance, in miles, each vehicle has traveled?

Ⓐ $\frac{3}{4} = \frac{3}{8}$ Ⓒ $\frac{3}{4} > \frac{3}{8}$

Ⓑ $\frac{3}{4} < \frac{3}{8}$ Ⓓ $\frac{3}{8} > \frac{3}{4}$

3. Juanita wrote number sentences to compare fractions. She made a mistake in one of her comparisons. Which statement is **not** true?

Ⓐ $\frac{3}{8} < \frac{5}{8}$ Ⓒ $\frac{2}{3} > \frac{2}{4}$

Ⓑ $\frac{4}{6} > \frac{4}{8}$ Ⓓ $\frac{3}{6} = \frac{1}{6}$

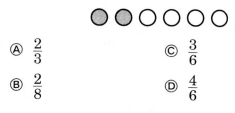

Name _____

1. Which fraction is less than the fraction shown by the shaded marbles?

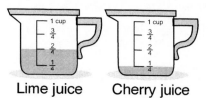

Ⓐ $\frac{2}{3}$ Ⓒ $\frac{3}{6}$

Ⓑ $\frac{2}{8}$ Ⓓ $\frac{4}{6}$

2. Cindy wants to make punch for her birthday party. Her punch recipe calls for $\frac{1}{4}$ cup cherry juice and $\frac{2}{4}$ cup lime juice as shown.

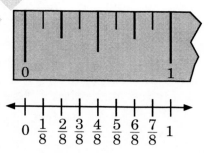

Lime juice   Cherry juice

Which number sentence is true about the amount, in cups, of cherry juice and lime juice in Cindy's punch?

Ⓐ $\frac{1}{4} = \frac{2}{4}$ Ⓒ $\frac{1}{4} > \frac{2}{4}$

Ⓑ $\frac{1}{4} < \frac{2}{4}$ Ⓓ $\frac{2}{4} < \frac{1}{4}$

3. Marie wrote number sentences to compare fractions. She made a mistake in one of her comparisons. Which statement is **not** true?

Ⓐ $\frac{7}{8} > \frac{5}{8}$ Ⓒ $\frac{3}{6} < \frac{3}{4}$

Ⓑ $\frac{5}{6} > \frac{5}{8}$ Ⓓ $\frac{2}{3} < \frac{1}{3}$

4. Zach finished $\frac{2}{3}$ of his homework before dinner. Zane finished $\frac{2}{4}$ of his homework before dinner. Which statement is true about the amount of homework completed before dinner?

Ⓐ Zane finished a greater fraction of his homework than Zach.

Ⓑ Zach finished a smaller fraction of his homework than Zane.

Ⓒ Zane finished a smaller fraction of his homework than Zach.

Ⓓ The two boys finished the same fraction of their homework.

5. Efrain drew a number line to help him understand the small marks on his customary ruler.

Which of the following number sentences is true?

Ⓐ $\frac{2}{8}$ in. $< \frac{5}{8}$ in.   Ⓒ $\frac{3}{8}$ in. $= \frac{4}{8}$ in.

Ⓑ $\frac{1}{8}$ in. $> \frac{7}{8}$ in.   Ⓓ $\frac{5}{8}$ in. $> \frac{6}{8}$ in.

6. Each day, Bethany drinks $\frac{3}{4}$ cup of orange juice for breakfast. Her younger brother drinks less juice than Bethany. Write a fraction that could represent the amount of juice Bethany's brother drinks.

Answer: _____

Justify your answer by drawing a model.

Analysis/Analyze

1. Fernando and Sarah each have candy bars that are the same size and shape. Fernando's candy bar is marked so that it can be broken into 8 equal rectangular pieces. Sarah's candy bar is marked so that it can be broken into 6 equal rectangular pieces. Fernando ate 4 of the rectangular pieces of his candy bar. Sarah also ate 4 of the rectangular pieces of her candy bar. Who ate the greater fraction of their candy bar?

   Answer: _____

   Justify your answer with words and pictures.

   _____

   _____

   _____

Analysis/Analyze

2. Judy knows that $\frac{5}{6}$ is greater than $\frac{5}{8}$ by looking at the denominators of the two fractions. She also knows that $\frac{5}{8}$ is greater than $\frac{3}{8}$. Use this information to write a number sentence comparing $\frac{5}{6}$ and $\frac{3}{8}$.

   Answer: _____

   Explain your reasoning. _____

   _____

Journal: Analysis/Analyze

Nicholas ate $\frac{1}{2}$ of a small pizza. Diana ate $\frac{1}{2}$ of a medium pizza. Alexi ate $\frac{1}{2}$ of a large pizza. Are all halves the same? Why or why not?

_____

_____

_____

_____

_____

Name _____

Fraction Compare Square

Use the fractions given to complete the *Fraction Compare Square*. The fractions should be placed so that each row shows fractions increasing in size from left to right. Each column should contain fractions that increase in size from top to bottom.

Fractions: $\dfrac{1}{4}$, $\dfrac{1}{6}$, $\dfrac{2}{4}$, $\dfrac{2}{8}$, $\dfrac{3}{6}$, $\dfrac{3}{8}$

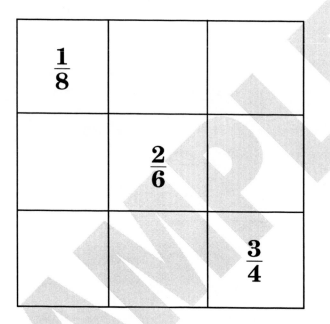

What do you notice about the fractions that appear on the diagonals?

_____

_____

Parent Activities

1. Using a tube of icing, have your child draw lines on sugar cookies to represent different fractional parts. The cookies can then be used to compare the fractions.

2. Fold 3 pieces of paper (same size, same shape) into thirds, fourths, and sixths. Color two parts of each paper. Write number sentences that compare the three fractions using < (less than), > (greater than), or =.

3. Turn dinner into a fraction lesson. Ask your child questions such as, "If I cut the pizza into 2 equal slices, what fraction is each slice? If I cut the pizza into 8 equal slices, what fraction is one slice? Which is larger, $\frac{1}{2}$ or $\frac{1}{8}$? Why?"

Level 3

Name _____

1. Mrs. Robbins' third-grade class eats lunch at the time shown on the clock.

What time is shown on the clock?

Answer: _____

2. Joseph finished his math homework at 5:30 p.m.

He started his homework 24 minutes earlier. At what time did Joseph start his homework?

Answer: _____

3. Abe is making cookies. He puts the cookies in the oven at 4:27. The cookies need to bake for fifteen minutes. At what time should Abe take the cookies out of the oven?

Answer: _____

When Abe checked the cookies, they were not quite baked. He let them bake until 4:46. How many more minutes did the cookies bake?

Answer: _____

4. At Chaucer Elementary School students who ride the bus are dismissed at the time shown on this clock.

The remaining students are dismissed 15 minutes later. What time are the remaining students dismissed?

Answer: _____

5. Draw hands so that this clock shows 3:16.

6. Mattie started softball practice at 4:15 p.m. At practice, she listened to her coach talk for 10 minutes, practiced batting for 25 minutes, and practiced fielding for a half hour. Use the number line to show how long Mattie's practice lasted.

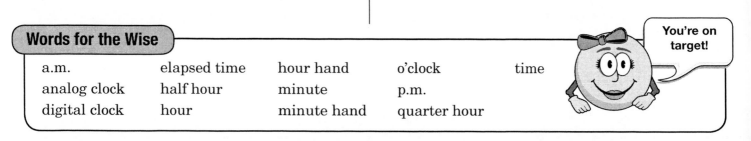

4:00   4:15   4:30   4:45   5:00   5:15   5:30

What time was Mattie's practice over?

Answer: _____

Words for the Wise

a.m.	elapsed time	hour hand	o'clock	time
analog clock	half hour	minute	p.m.	
digital clock	hour	minute hand	quarter hour	

You're on target!

⭐ partner practice

1. The school bus leaves the school each afternoon at the time shown on this clock.

What time does the school bus leave the school?

Ⓐ 3:07 p.m.   Ⓒ 2:15 p.m.

Ⓑ 3:05 p.m.   Ⓓ 2:03 p.m.

2. Look at the time shown on this clock.

Which is **not** a way to read the time shown on the clock?

Ⓐ eight thirty-three

Ⓑ 8:33

Ⓒ six forty

Ⓓ twenty-seven minutes before nine

3. Jasmine went swimming with her friend at 2:35 p.m. They swam for 43 minutes. What time did they stop swimming?

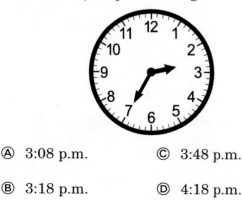

Ⓐ 3:08 p.m.   Ⓒ 3:48 p.m.

Ⓑ 3:18 p.m.   Ⓓ 4:18 p.m.

4. The Fernandez family finished eating dinner at the time shown on this clock. It took them a half hour to eat.

What time did they begin eating dinner?

Ⓐ 5:55 p.m.   Ⓒ 6:55 p.m.

Ⓑ 6:30 p.m.   Ⓓ 7:55 p.m.

5. Felicia arrived at the mall at 10:15 a.m. She spent a half hour trying on shoes, 45 minutes in the music store, and a quarter hour in the food court before leaving the mall. What time did Felicia leave the mall?

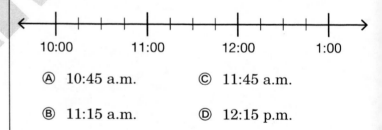

Ⓐ 10:45 a.m.   Ⓒ 11:45 a.m.

Ⓑ 11:15 a.m.   Ⓓ 12:15 p.m.

6. Mark began reading his library book at 4:09. He read until 4:45. How many minutes (min) did Mark read his library book?

Ⓐ 54 min

Ⓑ 46 min

Ⓒ 44 min

Ⓓ 36 min

         Level 3

1. The analog clock in the school gym shows this time.

What time would be shown on the digital scoreboard?

ⓐ 5:22   ⓒ 4:40

ⓑ 4:42   ⓓ 4:38

2. Which is **not** a way to read the time shown on this clock?

ⓐ three minutes before ten

ⓑ 9:57

ⓒ fifty-seven minutes past ten

ⓓ fifty-seven minutes past nine

3. Jacob began cleaning his room at 5:26 p.m. He finished the chore at 5:44 p.m. How many minutes (min) did Jacob spend cleaning his room?

ⓐ 18 min

ⓑ 20 min

ⓒ 28 min

ⓓ 70 min

4. Astrid must go to bed at 9:30 p.m. each school night. On Saturday nights, her parents allow her to stay up an extra 45 minutes. What time must Astrid go to bed on Saturday night?

ⓐ 10:45 p.m.   ⓒ 10:15 p.m.

ⓑ 10:30 p.m.   ⓓ 9:45 p.m.

5. Beckham finished soccer practice at 4:15 p.m. as shown on this clock.

If Beckham practiced for 55 minutes, at what time did practice begin?

ⓐ 4:00 p.m.   ⓒ 3:30 p.m.

ⓑ 3:55 p.m.   ⓓ 3:20 p.m.

6. Ingrid woke up at 6:55 a.m. She spent 25 minutes taking a bath and getting dressed. She took 15 minutes to eat her breakfast. She took another 10 minutes walking to school. What time did Ingrid arrive at school?

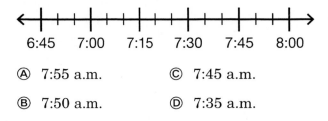

ⓐ 7:55 a.m.   ⓒ 7:45 a.m.

ⓑ 7:50 a.m.   ⓓ 7:35 a.m.

1. Look at the time shown on this analog clock.

Which digital clock matches this time?

Ⓐ **8:55**   Ⓒ **7:56**

Ⓑ **7:54**   Ⓓ **8:10**

2. Look at the time shown on this clock.

Which is **not** a way to read the time shown on the clock?

Ⓐ 3:36

Ⓑ twenty-four minutes before four

Ⓒ thirty-six minutes before four

Ⓓ thirty-six minutes after three

3. The ham Mrs. Thomas is preparing for dinner needs to cook for 45 minutes. Dinner is served at 7:00 p.m. What time should Mrs. Thomas begin cooking the ham?

Ⓐ 6:15 p.m.   Ⓒ 6:45 p.m.

Ⓑ 6:35 p.m.   Ⓓ 7:15 p.m.

4. Each morning Mrs. Campbell begins teaching her writing lesson at the time shown on this clock.

The writing lesson lasts 45 minutes. What time is the lesson over?

Ⓐ 9:45   Ⓒ 10:00

Ⓑ 9:50   Ⓓ 10:05

5. Math class began at 10:30. The students completed a facts drill sheet the first 10 minutes. The teacher taught for 15 minutes, and the students worked in math groups for a half hour before going to lunch. How long did the students spend in math class before going to lunch? Use the number line to find your answer.

Answer: _____

What time did the students go to lunch?

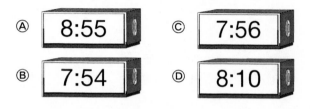

10:30   10:45   11:00   11:15   11:30   11:45

Answer: _____

Level 3

Analysis/Analyze —————————————————————————————————

1. Taffy gets home from school at 3:30 p.m. She eats dinner at 6:00 p.m.

Before dinner, Taffy practices flute for 1 hour, cleans her room for a half hour, and plays video games for 45 minutes. Does Taffy have at least a quarter hour to read her library book before dinner?

Answer: _____

Explain your answer. _____

_____

Analysis/Analyze —————————————————————————————————

2. Analyze the times shown on these clock faces. Write the time on the line below each clock. Extend the pattern to show the next time.

_____   _____   _____   _____

Explain how you found your answer._____

_____

Journal: Application/Apply ———————————————————————————

A quarter of a dollar is 25 cents. A quarter of an hour is 15 minutes. Explain why these values are different.

_____

_____

_____

_____

⭐ **motivation station**

Elapsed Time Travel

Play *Elapsed Time Travel* with a partner. Each player needs a game board with a token placed on the clock showing 3:00. Each pair of players needs 2 number cubes. Player 1 rolls the number cubes and spins the +/− spinner. The player multiplies the 2 numbers rolled to determine the number of minutes elapsed. The spinner shows if the elapsed time is counted forward (+) or backward (−). The player moves to the next clock and records the new time. Play passes to Player 2 and alternates until both players reach the Finish clock. The player whose Finish clock shows a time closest to 6:00 is the winner.

START

FINISH

Parent Activities

1. Help your child associate times and events (e.g., 8:30 p.m. bedtime, 11:45 a.m. lunchtime).

2. As you are cooking or driving, ask your child questions about time. "It is 3:15. If it takes 25 minutes to get home, what time will it be when we get there? This chicken has to cook for 1 hour 30 minutes. If I need to serve it at 7:00, what time do I need to start cooking?"

3. Provide your child with a calendar. Mark important dates. Ask calendar-related questions. "What month comes next? How many Thursdays are in this month? How many days until your birthday? What day comes after Tuesday?"

4. Look for pictures of clocks and watches in advertisements. What do you notice about these clocks?

 Level 3

1. A nickel has a mass of about 5 grams. Name one item that has a mass less than 5 grams.

   Answer: _____

   Name one item that has a mass greater than 5 grams.

   Answer: _____

2. Logan's estimate of the capacity of a juice box is 200 milliliters. Mason's estimate of its capacity is 200 liters. Which student has the best estimate of the capacity of a juice box?

   Answer: _____

3. List three containers that have a capacity greater than 1 liter.

   _____

   _____

   _____

4. Blake has a collection of 30 baseball cards. If each card has a mass of 2 grams, what is the total mass of all the cards? Show your work.

   Answer: _____

5. Corina knows that a nickel has a mass of about 5 grams. How could Corina use this information to find the approximate mass of the toy truck?

   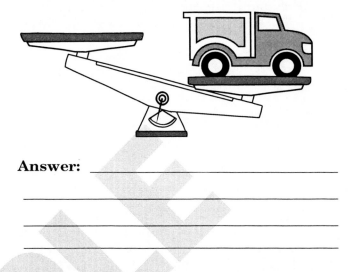

   Answer: _____

   _____

   _____

   _____

6. This figure shows two different liquids that a scientist used in an experiment.

   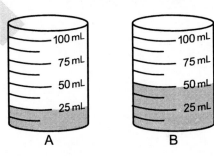

   Write an equation that can be used to find the total volume of liquid the scientist used.

   Answer: _____

   Would the total volume of liquid used be greater than or less than 1 liter?

   Answer: _____

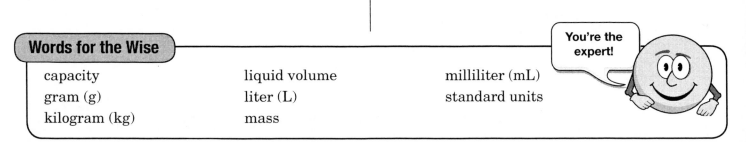

Words for the Wise

You're the expert!

capacity	liquid volume	milliliter (mL)
gram (g)	liter (L)	standard units
kilogram (kg)	mass	

⭐ **partner practice**

1. Seven students signed up to bring soda to the third-grade party. The teacher told the students they would need to bring a total of 35 liters (L). How many liters of soda should each student bring if they all bring the same amount?

Ⓐ 3 L

Ⓑ 5 L

Ⓒ 28 L

Ⓓ 42 L

2. Mr. Dillard's children compared the masses of their pets. Samuel's Great Dane has a mass of 78 kilograms (kg), while William's Siamese cat has a mass of 7 kilograms. Jasmine has a poodle with a mass of 29 kilograms. How much greater is the mass of the Great Dane than the total mass of the poodle and the cat?

Ⓐ 36 kg

Ⓑ 42 kg

Ⓒ 49 kg

Ⓓ 114 kg

3. Grow & Feed is a solution that helps flowers sprout quickly and stay healthy. Mariah wants to try the solution on 4 pots of flowers on her back porch. The directions say to pour 35 milliliters (mL) of the solution into each flower pot. Which is the best estimate of how much Grow & Feed solution Mariah will use?

Ⓐ 40 mL

Ⓑ 70 mL

Ⓒ 160 mL

Ⓓ 350 mL

4. In order for this scale to be balanced, what is the mass, in grams (g), of package A?

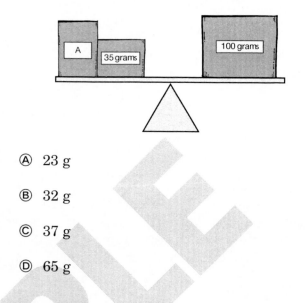

Ⓐ 23 g

Ⓑ 32 g

Ⓒ 37 g

Ⓓ 65 g

5. Charles combined 425 milliliters (mL) of iced tea, 160 milliliters of lemonade, and 245 milliliters of orange drink to make spiced tea. How much spiced tea did Charles make?

Ⓐ 585 mL

Ⓑ 640 mL

Ⓒ 820 mL

Ⓓ 830 mL

6. Mrs. Jackson's goal for the year is to lose weight. She needs to lose 18 kilograms (kg) in four months. Which is the best estimate of the number of kilograms Mrs. Jackson should plan to lose each month?

Ⓐ 5 kg

Ⓑ 14 kg

Ⓒ 20 kg

Ⓓ 80 kg

1. Paul is making a single serving of fruit punch. He has 25 milliliters of lemon juice, 100 milliliters of water, 50 milliliters of pineapple juice, and 75 milliliters of orange juice. Which combination of liquids will exactly fill a 200 milliliter measuring cup?

orange juice   pineapple juice   water   lemon juice

Ⓐ orange juice, pineapple juice, and water

Ⓑ orange juice, pineapple juice, and lemon juice

Ⓒ orange juice, water, and lemon juice

Ⓓ pineapple juice, water, and lemon juice

2. Mary is buying packages of soup mix. Each package has a mass of 40 grams (g). What would be the mass of 9 packages of soup mix?

Ⓐ 31 g

Ⓑ 49 g

Ⓒ 270 g

Ⓓ 360 g

3. Addie used 2 kilograms (kg) of flour to make 6 loaves of bread. How many kilograms of flour will Addie need to make 12 loaves of bread?

Ⓐ 12 kg

Ⓑ 8 kg

Ⓒ 6 kg

Ⓓ 4 kg

4. Lawrence ordered a large drink with his hamburger. Which is the most reasonable capacity of Lawrence's large drink?

Ⓐ 1 milliliter

Ⓑ 10 milliliters

Ⓒ 1 liter

Ⓓ 10 liters

5. Which item is most likely to have a mass of 1 gram?

Ⓐ

Ⓑ

Ⓒ

Ⓓ

6. In science class, Martin poured 197 milliliters (mL) of water into his beaker. Edwin poured 169 milliliters of water into his beaker. How much more water did Martin pour into his beaker than Edwin?

Ⓐ 42 mL

Ⓑ 38 mL

Ⓒ 36 mL

Ⓓ 28 mL

assessment

1. Mrs. Castello uses a 4-liter bucket to water the plants in her garden. She fills the bucket 8 times each time she waters her garden. Which equation shows how many liters of water Mrs. Castello uses when she waters her garden?

   (A) $8 ÷ 4 = 2$ (C) $8 + 4 = 12$

   (B) $8 - 4 = 4$ (D) $8 × 4 = 32$

2. Lisa calculated that 5 medium apples have a mass of about 1 kilogram (kg). At the farmers' market, she bought this basket of apples. What would be the approximate mass of the basket of apples?

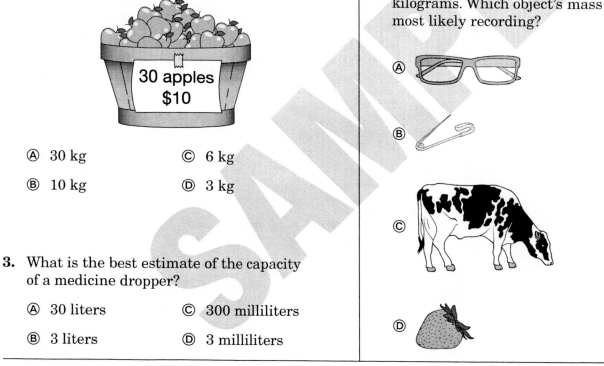

   30 apples
   $10

   (A) 30 kg   (C) 6 kg

   (B) 10 kg   (D) 3 kg

3. What is the best estimate of the capacity of a medicine dropper?

   (A) 30 liters   (C) 300 milliliters

   (B) 3 liters   (D) 3 milliliters

4. The mass of a tennis ball is 57 grams (g). Peyton thinks his lucky number is 6, so he always takes exactly 6 tennis balls when he plays tennis. What is the best estimate of the mass of the tennis balls Peyton takes to a tennis match?

   (A) 500 g

   (B) 360 g

   (C) 300 g

   (D) 63 g

5. Rowena is recording an object's mass in kilograms. Which object's mass is Rowena most likely recording?

   (A)

   (B)

   (C)

   (D)

6. The high school concession stand keeps track of the amount of beverages sold at the Friday night football games. Last week, they sold 457 liters of soda, 231 liters of lemonade, and 129 liters of water. How much more soda was sold than lemonade and water combined? Show your work.

   Answer: _____

 Level 3

Application/Apply

1. Look at the toy car on the balance scale. What is the mass of the car?

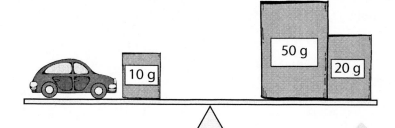

    Answer: _____

    Explain your answer with words and numbers. _____

    _____

    _____

Analysis/Analyze

2. Adelle has one 550-gram jar of peanut butter. She needs exactly 500 grams of peanut butter for one batch of cookies. Adelle is making three batches of cookies for the school bake sale. She went to the store and bought a 725-gram jar of peanut butter. Will Adelle have enough peanut butter to make the cookies?

    Answer: _____

    Explain your answer using numbers and words. _____

    _____

    _____

Journal: Analysis/Analyze

The prefix "kilo" means 1000. A kilogram is equal to 1000 grams.
Using this information, explain what a kiloliter is.

_____

_____

_____

_____

★ **motivation station**

Think It Through

Anderson had to put 6 pumpkins in order by mass. He could only use a balance scale. He compared the pumpkins and sketched the different comparisons. Look at Anderson's sketches. Use the sketches to put the pumpkins in order from greatest mass to least mass.

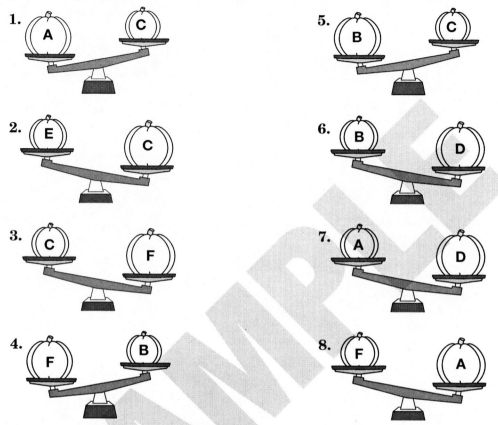

Write the letters in the pumpkins from greatest mass to least mass.

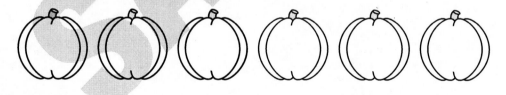

Parent Activities

1. Have your child read the labels on the juice, water, and milk containers in your refrigerator. Discuss how many milliliters and/or liters the containers hold. Measure the amounts of liquid left in the containers after some of the liquids have been consumed. Help your child determine how much liquid was consumed from the containers.

2. Many canned foods have the mass listed in grams. Find several different canned items and have your child find the total mass.

3. The grocery store is a good place for estimating and weighing. Have your child estimate the masses of fruits and vegetables in grams and/or kilograms. Then place the items on the grocery scale to see the actual mass.

 Level 3 ©2012–2014 MentoringMinds.com

Name _____

Use this graph to answer questions 1 – 3.

The students at Winston School voted on the field trips they wanted to take during the school year. The graph shows the number of students who voted for each field trip. Each student was allowed to vote for only one field trip.

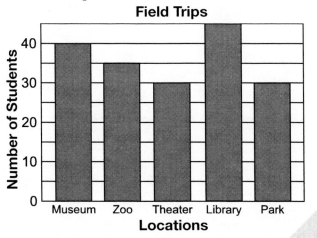

Field Trips

1. How many more students voted for the museum than the park?

   Answer: _____

2. What is the total number of students who voted in this survey? Show your work.

   Answer: _____

3. Based on the information on the graph, write a true statement about the field trip vote.

   _____

   _____

Use this picture graph to answer questions 4 – 6.

Belinda made a picture graph showing the 60 different flowers she planted in her garden.

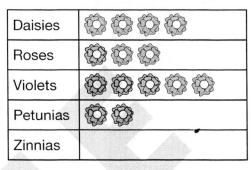

Flowers Planted in the Garden

Daisies	
Roses	
Violets	
Petunias	
Zinnias	

Key
🌸 represents 3 flowers

4. Belinda forgot to record the number of zinnias she planted. Using the graph scale, determine how many zinnias Belinda planted and complete her picture graph.

5. How many more violets than petunias did Belinda plant in her garden? Show your work.

   Answer: _____

6. Which type of flower did Belinda plant in greater numbers than petunias but in fewer numbers than daisies?

   Answer: _____

Words for the Wise

bar graph	key	scale
data	picture graph	

Never give up!

★ partner practice

1. The graph shows the number of books read by 4 students. How many more books did Jo read than Ben?

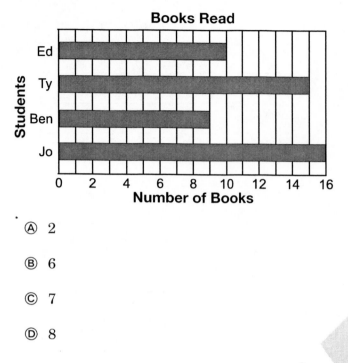

Books Read

Ⓐ 2

Ⓑ 6

Ⓒ 7

Ⓓ 8

2. The third graders at Douglas Elementary voted for their favorite animals. The graph shows the number of students who voted for each animal.

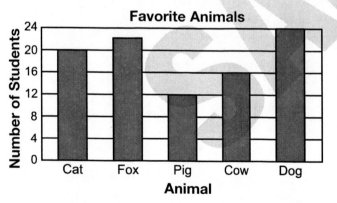

How many more students voted for foxes than for cows?

Ⓐ 38

Ⓑ 10

Ⓒ 6

Ⓓ 2

Use this graph to answer questions 3 – 5.

The graph shows the favorite subjects of the students in Mrs. Knight's class.

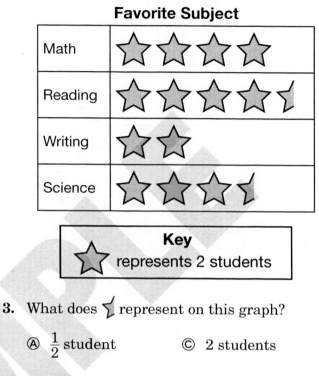

3. What does 🌟 represent on this graph?

Ⓐ $\frac{1}{2}$ student   Ⓒ 2 students

Ⓑ 1 student   Ⓓ 3 students

4. What is the total number of students in Mrs. Knight's class?

Ⓐ 28   Ⓒ 15

Ⓑ 26   Ⓓ 14

5. Based on the graph, which statement about Mrs. Knight's class is true?

Ⓐ More students like writing than math.

Ⓑ Four students chose math as their favorite subject.

Ⓒ Each star on the graph represents 4 students.

Ⓓ Twenty-four students did not choose writing as their favorite subject.

          Level 3   ©2012–2014 MentoringMinds.com

1. The Toy Palace has four shelves of teddy bears. The graph shows how many teddy bears are on each shelf.

Toy Palace Teddy Bears

Key
represents 4 teddy bears

How many teddy bears does the Toy Palace have on Shelf 1 and Shelf 3?

ⓐ 11   ⓒ 42

ⓑ 21   ⓓ 44

2. The bar graph shows the amount of time Andrea and Mitchell spent walking their dogs last week.

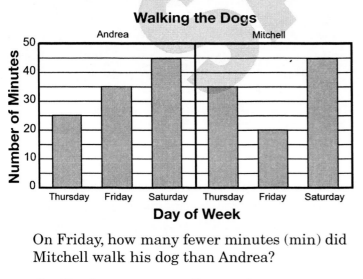

On Friday, how many fewer minutes (min) did Mitchell walk his dog than Andrea?

ⓐ 15 min   ⓒ 30 min

ⓑ 20 min   ⓓ 35 min

3. Movies-4-Us counted their children's videos. They have 7 cartoons, 6 fairy tales, 5 dramas, and 9 animal movies. Which bar graph correctly shows this information?

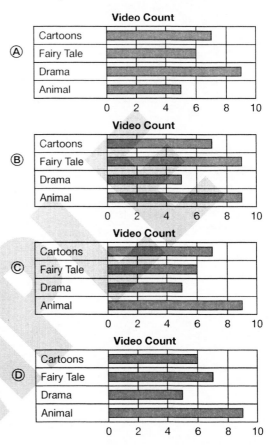

4. Mrs. Lima's class made a graph of the number of letters received from their pen pals each month. How many total letters did the class receive during Months 2, 4, and 5?

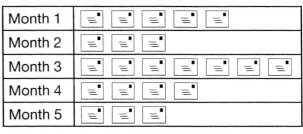

Letters Received

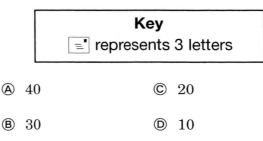

Key
represents 3 letters

ⓐ 40   ⓒ 20

ⓑ 30   ⓓ 10

1. The graph shows favorite types of music chosen by teachers at Bass Elementary.

Favorite Music

Rock & Roll	♪ ♪ ♪ ♪ ♪ ♪
Soul	♪ ♪ ♪
Country	♪ ♪ ♪ ♪
Classical	♪ ♪ ♪ ♪ ♪

Key

♪ represents 3 teachers

How many fewer teachers chose soul music and country music than classical music and rock and roll?

Ⓐ 9   Ⓒ 21

Ⓑ 12   Ⓓ 33

2. The bar graph shows the amount of time Arturo and Victor spent playing games last week.

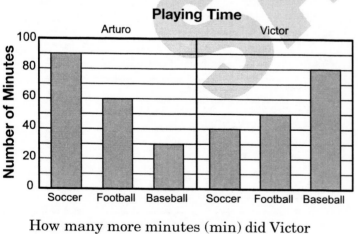

How many more minutes (min) did Victor spend playing baseball than Arturo?

Ⓐ 110 min   Ⓒ 20 min

Ⓑ 50 min   Ⓓ 10 min

3. The graph shows how many forks were needed in the cafeteria by each third-grade class.

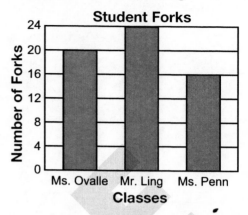

Which statement about the graph is **not** true?

Ⓐ Mr. Ling's class needed the most forks.

Ⓑ Ms. Penn's class needed 16 forks.

Ⓒ Ms. Ovalle's class needed 22 forks.

Ⓓ Three third-grade classes needed forks.

4. Four friends collected sand dollars at the beach. Deanna found 9, Marco found 12, Keysha found 15, and Sammir found 6. They made this picture graph of their data.

Sand Dollar Collections

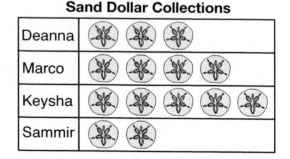

The friends did not make a key for the picture graph. Create a key in this rectangle that correctly completes the picture graph.

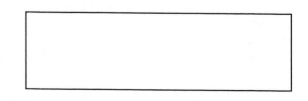

         Level 3

Name _____

Analysis/Analyze

1. The 26 students in Mrs. Smith's third-grade class voted for their favorite ice cream flavors. The choices were vanilla, chocolate, strawberry, and rocky road. Use the information to complete the picture graph.

   • Only 3 students chose rocky road as their favorite ice cream.
   • Twice as many students chose chocolate as strawberry.
   • Two more students selected strawberry than rocky road.
   • The number of students who chose vanilla was the same as the total number of students who chose rocky road and strawberry.

Favorite Ice Cream Flavors

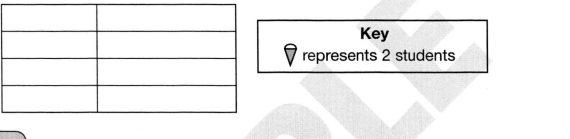

Key
🍦 represents 2 students

Analysis/Analyze

2. Fran and 3 friends made a bar graph to show how many baseball cards they have. The four friends have a total of 360 baseball cards. Sidney has the most with 110 cards.

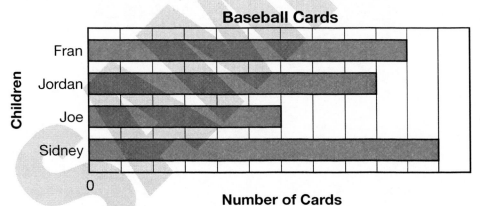

Baseball Cards

Children

Fran

Jordan

Joe

Sidney

0

Number of Cards

What numbers are missing from the scale at the bottom of the graph? Write the numbers on the graph. Explain how you found your answer.

_____

_____

Journal: Evaluation/Evaluate

Ethan wants to make a graph showing the different types of transportation used by students to get to school. Should Ethan use a bar graph or a picture graph? Justify your answer.

_____

_____

_____

Raise the Bar

Play *Raise the Bar* with a partner. Each pair of players needs a game sheet, a marker or crayon, and a dot cube. One player selects *even,* and the other player selects *odd.* In turn, each player rolls the dot cube. If an even number is rolled, the player who selected *even* shades a square on the even column. If an odd number is rolled, the player who selected *odd* shades a square on the odd column. The winner is the first person to shade all squares in his/her column.

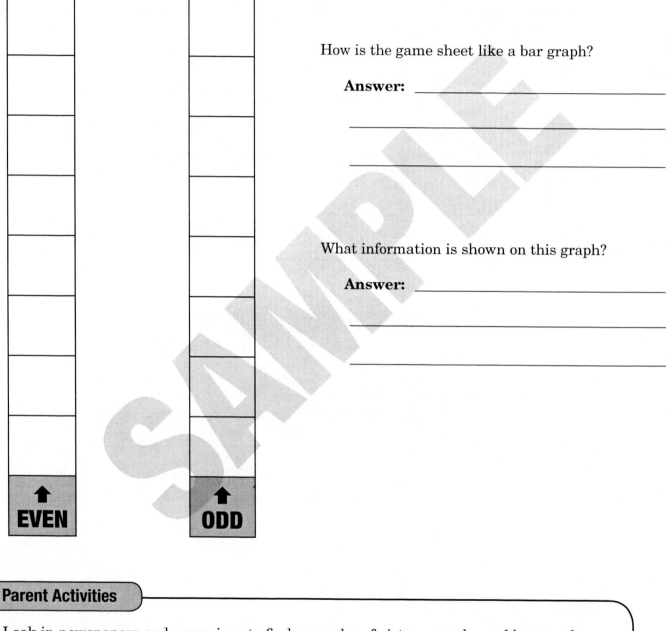

EVEN

ODD

How is the game sheet like a bar graph?

Answer: _____

_____

_____

What information is shown on this graph?

Answer: _____

_____

_____

Parent Activities

1. Look in newspapers and magazines to find examples of picture graphs and bar graphs. Discuss the scale on each graph, the symbols used in picture graphs, the labels, etc. Ask your child questions about the information on the graphs (e.g., "The key shows that this smiley face stands for 10 people. How could 5 people be represented?").

2. Make family graphs of information (e.g., shoe sizes, heights, arm spans). Have your child make up questions to be answered using the data on the graphs.

Name _____

1. Kubel's Furniture Store places sale tags on all items for their annual clearance sale. A sale tag is shown in this diagram.

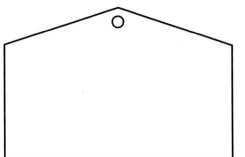

Use a ruler to measure the bottom of the sale tag. To the nearest half inch, what is the length of the bottom of the tag?

Answer: _____ inches

To the nearest quarter inch, how long is the right side of the tag?

Answer: _____ inches

2. Coach James wants each of his soccer players to measure the length of a foot to the nearest quarter inch to get a perfect fit for their soccer shoes. The line plot shows the measurements.

Soccer Team Foot Lengths

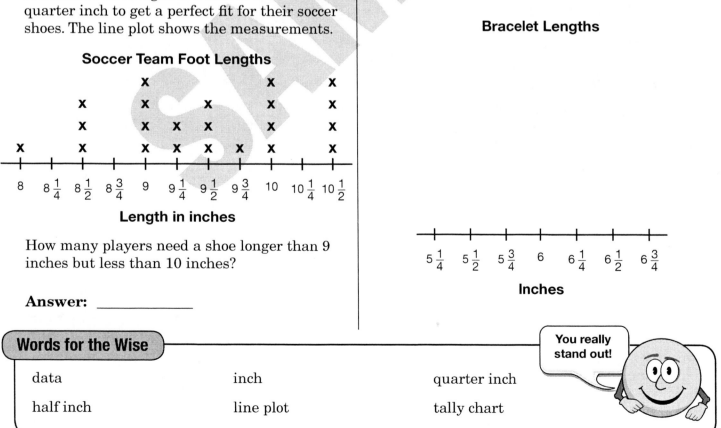

How many players need a shoe longer than 9 inches but less than 10 inches?

Answer: _____

3. What is the length of the paper clip?

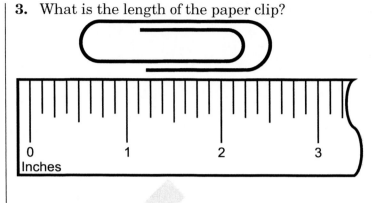

Answer: _____ inches

4. Mary's mother arranges her bracelets according to lengths. She made this tally chart to show the different lengths she has.

Length	$5\frac{1}{2}$	$5\frac{3}{4}$	6	$6\frac{1}{4}$	$6\frac{1}{2}$
Tally	IIII	II	₦Ⱥ	III	I

Use this information to complete the line plot.

Bracelet Lengths

$5\frac{1}{4}$ $5\frac{1}{2}$ $5\frac{3}{4}$ 6 $6\frac{1}{4}$ $6\frac{1}{2}$ $6\frac{3}{4}$

Inches

Words for the Wise

data	inch	quarter inch
half inch	line plot	tally chart

You really stand out!

★ partner practice

1. Happy Time Day Care gives its students two crackers at snack time as shown in the diagram.

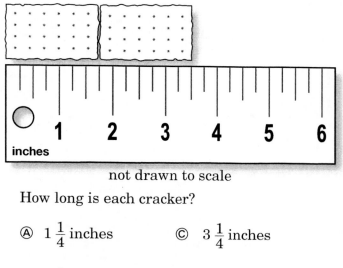

not drawn to scale

How long is each cracker?

Ⓐ $1\frac{1}{4}$ inches Ⓒ $3\frac{1}{4}$ inches

Ⓑ $1\frac{3}{4}$ inches Ⓓ $3\frac{1}{2}$ inches

2. William wants to build a display case for his model car collection. He uses a tape measure to measure the length, in inches (in.), of the longest model in his collection.

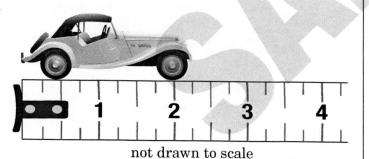

not drawn to scale

The display case will be divided into identical rectangular sections that will hold one model car each. What should be the length of each section in William's display case?

Ⓐ $1\frac{1}{2}$ in. Ⓒ 2 in.

Ⓑ $1\frac{3}{4}$ in. Ⓓ $2\frac{1}{2}$ in.

Use the data on the line plot to answer questions 3 – 5.

Students on Coach Peterson's track team earn points for walking laps before or after school. Students must walk four laps to earn credit for one mile (mi.). After one week, the coach made a line plot showing how many miles each student walked.

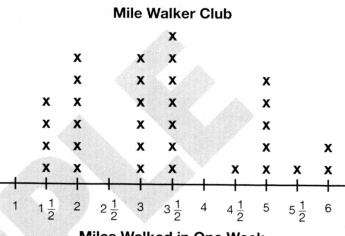

Mile Walker Club

Miles Walked in One Week

3. How many students walked at least 3 miles in one week?

Ⓐ 6 Ⓒ 18

Ⓑ 10 Ⓓ 22

4. What was the total distance walked by the top two students?

Ⓐ $17\frac{1}{2}$ mi. Ⓒ 12 mi.

Ⓑ 17 mi. Ⓓ 2 mi.

5. How many more students walked less than 4 miles than students who walked more than 4 miles?

Ⓐ 9 Ⓒ 14

Ⓑ 12 Ⓓ 23

 Level 3

1. Kendra needs to hammer a nail through a board that measures $\frac{3}{4}$ inch thick. The nail needs to go completely through the board and into the wall. Which of these nails would be **best** for Kendra to use?

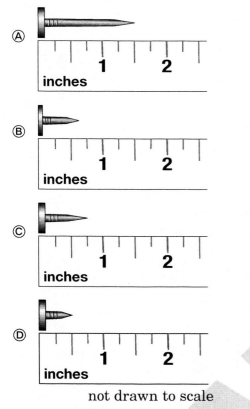

Ⓐ

inches

Ⓑ

inches

Ⓒ

inches

Ⓓ

inches

not drawn to scale

2. Molly wants to display her grandfather's pocket watch under a glass dome.

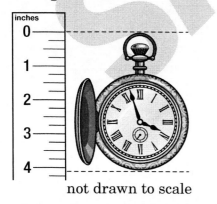

not drawn to scale

If the watch is to fit completely under the dome, which could be the height of the glass dome?

Ⓐ $2\frac{3}{4}$ in.   Ⓒ 4 in.

Ⓑ $3\frac{1}{4}$ in.   Ⓓ $4\frac{1}{4}$ in.

Use the line plot to answer questions 3 and 4.

Claire makes necklaces to sell online. The necklaces come in different lengths. This line plot shows how many of each necklace Claire sold in one week.

Necklaces Sold This Week

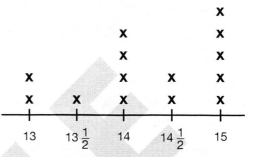

Length of Necklace (inches)

3. Which tally chart matches the data shown in the line plot?

Ⓐ

Length of Necklace (inches)	Number of Necklaces Sold
13	II
$13\frac{1}{2}$	I
14	IIII
$14\frac{1}{2}$	III
15	ЖI

Ⓒ

Length of Necklace (inches)	Number of Necklaces Sold
13	I
$13\frac{1}{2}$	II
14	ЖI
$14\frac{1}{2}$	II
15	IIII

Ⓑ

Length of Necklace (inches)	Number of Necklaces Sold
13	II
$13\frac{1}{2}$	II
14	III
$14\frac{1}{2}$	II
15	ЖI

Ⓓ

Length of Necklace (inches)	Number of Necklaces Sold
13	II
$13\frac{1}{2}$	I
14	IIII
$14\frac{1}{2}$	II
15	ЖI

4. How many necklaces sold are longer than 14 inches?

Ⓐ 11   Ⓒ 5

Ⓑ 7   Ⓓ 2

Name _____

1. Which pen is about $2\frac{1}{2}$ inches long? Use a ruler to measure.

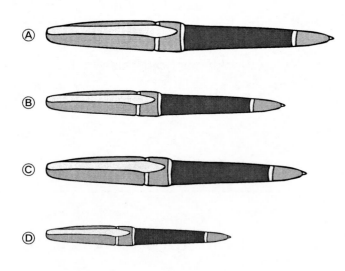

Ⓐ

Ⓑ

Ⓒ

Ⓓ

2. Measure the pens above. To the nearest half inch (in.), what is the difference between the longest and shortest pens?

Ⓐ 2 in.   Ⓒ 1 in.

Ⓑ $1\frac{1}{2}$ in.   Ⓓ $\frac{1}{2}$ in.

3. A teacher posts a sign next to her electric pencil sharpener. As she introduces a new rule to her class, she instructs the students to measure their pencils and record the lengths on the line plot below.

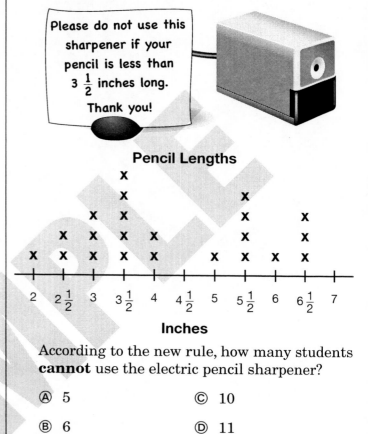

Please do not use this sharpener if your pencil is less than $3\frac{1}{2}$ inches long. Thank you!

Pencil Lengths

```
                    X
                    X              X
              X     X        X     X     X
        X     X     X   X    X     X     X
  X     X     X     X   X    X  X  X  X  X
  +---+---+---+---+---+---+---+---+---+---+
  2  2½   3  3½   4  4½   5  5½   6  6½   7
```
Inches

According to the new rule, how many students **cannot** use the electric pencil sharpener?

Ⓐ 5   Ⓒ 10

Ⓑ 6   Ⓓ 11

4. Custom Cabinet Shop uses different sized nails to build cabinets. The owner of the cabinet shop created a table to show how many boxes of each size nail are in stock.

Length of Nails (inches)	1	$1\frac{1}{4}$	$1\frac{1}{2}$	$1\frac{3}{4}$	2	$2\frac{1}{4}$	$2\frac{1}{2}$	$2\frac{3}{4}$
Boxes of Nails In Stock	III	ⅣⅣ I	IIII		II	ⅣⅣ	I	III

Use the information in the tally chart to create a line plot. Be sure to include a title and a label.

Illegal to copy   Level 3   ©2012–2014 MentoringMinds.com

Name _____

Analysis/Analyze

1. Sally placed two cubes beside each other as shown.

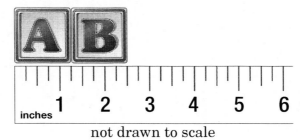

not drawn to scale

If Sally makes a tower that is 4 cubes tall, what would be the height of the stack?

Answer: _____ inches

Synthesis/Create

2. Find and measure eight items in your classroom that are less than 6 inches long. Measure each item to the nearest $\frac{1}{4}$ inch. Use your data to create a line plot. Be sure to provide a title, labels, and a key.

Write a question that can be solved using the data on your line plot.

_____

_____

Journal: Analysis/Analyze

Jaylon has a 6-inch ruler on his desk. His teacher noticed a marker above the ruler and asked him to measure the length of his marker without moving it. How could Jaylon determine the length of his marker?

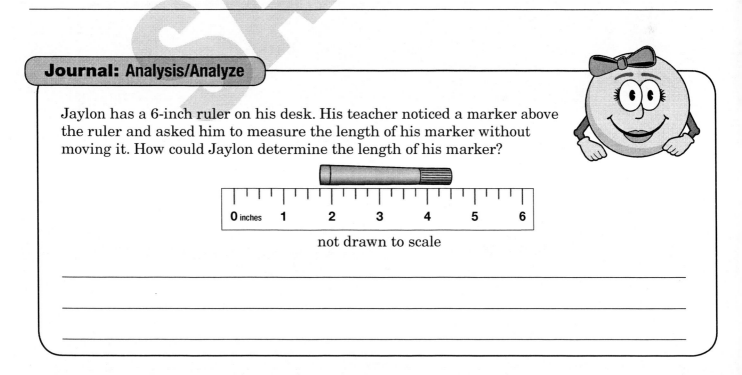

not drawn to scale

_____

_____

_____

Name _____

Measuring Me

Collect data by measuring the length of each of your fingers to the nearest quarter inch. Record the data on the hands outlined below.

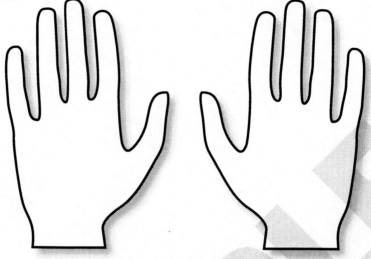

Create a line plot using the measurements of your 10 fingers.

Measuring Me

Finger Lengths (inches)
x = 1 finger

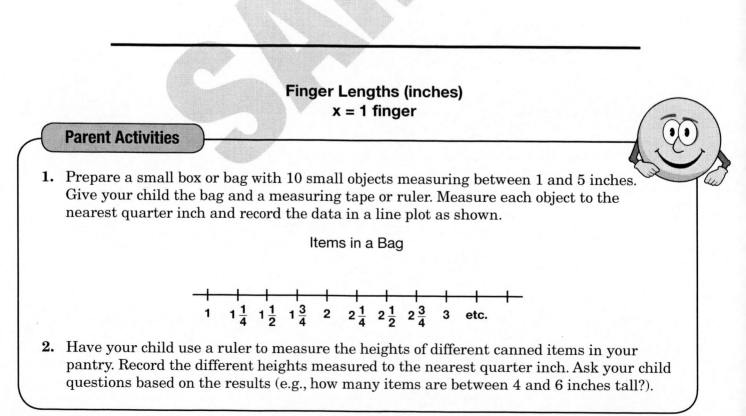

Parent Activities

1. Prepare a small box or bag with 10 small objects measuring between 1 and 5 inches. Give your child the bag and a measuring tape or ruler. Measure each object to the nearest quarter inch and record the data in a line plot as shown.

    Items in a Bag

    $1 \quad 1\frac{1}{4} \quad 1\frac{1}{2} \quad 1\frac{3}{4} \quad 2 \quad 2\frac{1}{4} \quad 2\frac{1}{2} \quad 2\frac{3}{4} \quad 3$ etc.

2. Have your child use a ruler to measure the heights of different canned items in your pantry. Record the different heights measured to the nearest quarter inch. Ask your child questions based on the results (e.g., how many items are between 4 and 6 inches tall?).

 Level 3

Name _____

1. Mrs. Worley placed a set of color tiles and a set of pattern blocks on her students' desks. She asked the students which of the two sets would best be used to measure the area of a desk top. How would you answer Mrs. Worley's question? Explain your answer.

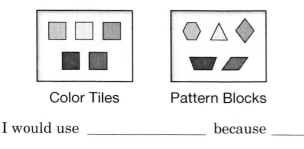

Color Tiles   Pattern Blocks

I would use _____ because _____

_____

_____ .

2. Joe and Larry each baked a pan of brownies to take to the school party. The boys cut the pans of brownies into different size squares as shown.

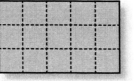 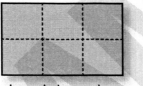

Joe's brownies   Larry's brownies

What was the area of Joe's brownies?

_____

What was the area of Larry's brownies?

_____

Both pans were the same shape and size. Why were the numbers of square units different?

_____

_____

3. Jasmine and Humberto want to find the area of an index card. Jasmine uses triangular tiles. Humberto uses square tiles. Which student used the best method to find the area? Use words and pictures to explain your answer.

Answer: _____

_____

_____

4. Mr. Jefferson wants to cover the top of an outdoor table with colorful tiles. He measures the table top and finds that it measures 5 feet in length and 4 feet in width. Mr. Jefferson bought square tiles that measured 1 foot on each side. How many tiles will Mr. Jefferson need to complete the project?

Answer: _____ tiles

Draw a diagram of the table top on the grid and show the solution to this problem.

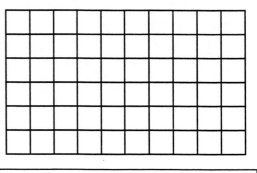

Key
☐ represents 1 square foot (ft.²)

Words for the Wise

area	square centimeter (cm²)	square meter (m²)
attribute	square foot (ft.²)	square unit
plane figure	square inch (in.²)	

Remarkable job!

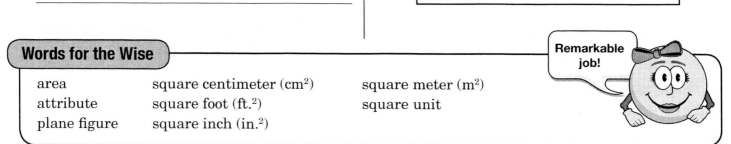

★ **partner practice**

1. Which of the following tiles **cannot** be used to find the area of this rectangle in square units?

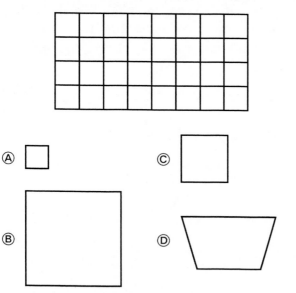

Ⓐ Ⓒ

Ⓑ Ⓓ

2. Eric and Tim covered index cards with tiles and then counted the tiles to find the areas. Their tilings are shown.

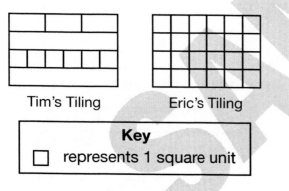

Tim's Tiling   Eric's Tiling

Key
☐ represents 1 square unit

Which statement is true?

Ⓐ Both boys will get an accurate answer because they used rectangular tiles.

Ⓑ Neither boy will get a correct answer because the tiles are too small.

Ⓒ Tim will get the best answer because he used tiles of different sizes.

Ⓓ Eric will get the best answer because he used identical square tiles.

3. Lucy's teacher asked each student to bring items with areas that could be measured in square units. Lucy brought a magazine, a piece of string, a framed picture, and a bookmark. Which of these items would **not** be measured in square units?

Ⓐ magazine cover   Ⓒ framed picture

Ⓑ string   Ⓓ bookmark

4. Jenny and Julie lived in apartments with identical floor plans. They discovered that they had different tile patterns covering the floors in their kitchens. Their kitchen floor patterns are shown.

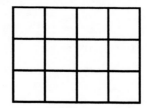

Jenny's Kitchen Tiles   Julie's Kitchen Tiles

Which statement is true?

Ⓐ The area of Jenny's kitchen floor is 12 square units.

Ⓑ The area of Julie's kitchen floor is greater than Jenny's.

Ⓒ Julie's kitchen tiles are the best units to use for finding area.

Ⓓ The area of Julie's kitchen floor is 18 square units.

     Level 3

1. Jamal's mother is baking a dessert that requires the bottom of her rectangular baking pan to be lined with cookies. Which shape of cookie can she **best** use to line the pan without leaving any open spaces and without overlapping the cookies?

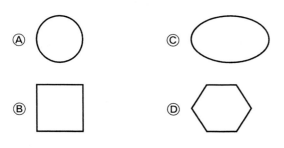

4. KayLynn took these photographs of patterns she saw on her daily walk. Which of KayLynn's pictures represents a surface covered with square units?

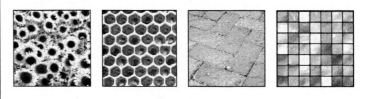

Ⓐ flower bed   Ⓒ brick street

Ⓑ honeycomb   Ⓓ tile wall

2. Mrs. Taylor wants to replace the carpet in her living room. She went to the carpet store to select the new carpet. The salesman asked her a question. Which of these questions does Mrs. Taylor need to answer before she can buy new carpet?

Ⓐ How many windows are in the living room?

Ⓑ What is the height of the ceiling in the living room?

Ⓒ What is the area in square feet of the living room floor?

Ⓓ What is the perimeter of the living room floor?

5. A teacher divided her class into 3 teams. She challenged each team to find the area of a poster with different pattern blocks. Team One chose green triangles to cover the poster. Team Two chose orange square tiles, and Team Three chose yellow hexagons. Which team will most accurately determine the area of the poster in square inches?

Ⓐ Team One   Ⓒ Team Three

Ⓑ Team Two   Ⓓ None of the teams

3. Kelly wants to find the area of the front cover of her library book. Which of the following shows a correct way Kelly could find the area in square units?

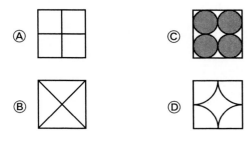

6. Marcus is using this unit square to cover the top of his desk.

Which of these is Marcus most likely measuring?

Ⓐ the weight of his desk

Ⓑ the thickness of his desktop

Ⓒ the area of his desktop

Ⓓ the height of his desktop

★ assessment

1. Which unit would **best** be used when trying to determine the area of a lawn?

   Ⓐ square centimeters

   Ⓑ square inches

   Ⓒ square feet

   Ⓓ square miles

2. Derek's family wants to tile the floor in their playroom. They selected two different designs at Tile World.

   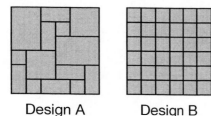

   Design A   Design B

   Which design covers the area of the floor in unit squares?

   Ⓐ Design A only

   Ⓑ Design B only

   Ⓒ Both Design A and Design B

   Ⓓ Neither Design A nor Design B

3. Mr. Chance challenged his students to find a rectangle in the classroom with an area of 9 square units. Which student won the challenge?

   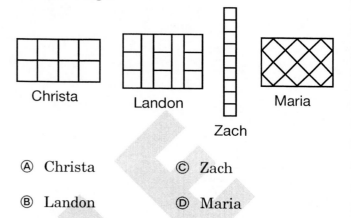

   Christa   Landon   Zach   Maria

   Ⓐ Christa   Ⓒ Zach

   Ⓑ Landon   Ⓓ Maria

4. Which statement about area is **not** true?

   Ⓐ Square units can be used to measure the area of a figure.

   Ⓑ A plane figure must be covered without gaps to measure the area.

   Ⓒ The units covering a figure must not overlap when measuring area.

   Ⓓ Triangular tiles are the best unit to use when finding the area of a figure.

5. One rainy afternoon, Leslie, Saul, and Micah decided to create their own game boards. These are the game boards they created.

      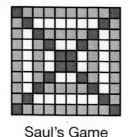   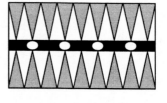

   Leslie's Game   Saul's Game   Micah's Game

   Which friend created a game board with an area that could be most easily measured in square units?

   Answer: _____

   Explain why the other game boards would **not** be most easily measured in square units.

   _____

   _____

Name _____

Analysis/Analyze

1. Lisa made this poster to help remember the difference between area and perimeter.

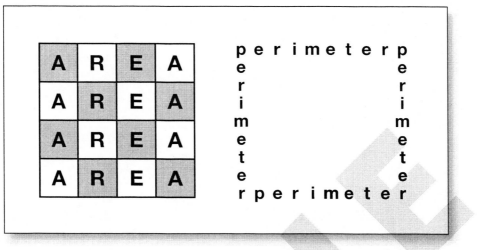

Explain Lisa's poster. _____

_____

Analysis/Analyze

2. Mr. Arroyo owns a carpet store. He sells carpet by the square foot. Mr. Arroyo went to a customer's house to measure a room for carpet and drew this sketch of the floor of the room.

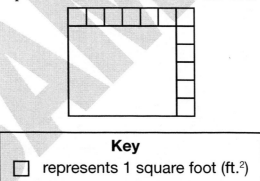

Key

☐ represents 1 square foot (ft.^{2})

How can Mr. Arroyo determine the area of the room? _____

_____

_____

Journal: Evaluation/Evaluate

Explain 2 reasons why the area of a plane figure is best measured in square units.

1. _____

_____

2. _____

_____

★ **motivation station**

Build a Fence

Play *Build a Fence* with a partner. Each pair of players needs the game sheet and 2 number cubes. Player 1 tosses the number cubes and makes a fence on the grid by marking the length on a horizontal line using the number on one cube and the width on a vertical line using the number on the other cube. The player then outlines the entire rectangle to make a fence. The player records the number of rows in the length and the number of columns in the width and the area that is fenced, in square units. Play then passes to Player 2. Players continue for 4 rounds. After round 4, a player's total score is determined by the sum of the areas. The player with the highest score wins.

Player 1

	Rows	Columns	Area in square units
Round 1			
Round 2			
Round 3			
Round 4			

Total Score
_____

Player 2

	Rows	Columns	Area in square units
Round 1			
Round 2			
Round 3			
Round 4			

Total Score
_____

Parent Activities

1. Find square tiles in your house (e.g., on the kitchen floor, bathroom tiles, etc.), and discuss how they can be used to measure areas in your house. Talk about why square tiles are better for finding area than circular tiles.

2. Have your child find the areas of the tops of different items in your home (e.g., kitchen table, end table, coffee table, etc.) by covering them with square sticky notes.

Name _____

1. Penny made this quilt pattern.

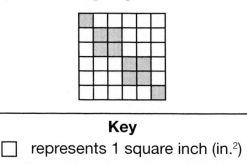

Key

☐ represents 1 square inch (in.²)

What is the area of the shaded part of Penny's quilt pattern?

Answer: _____

2. Randall covered the top of his desk with square tiles.

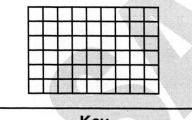

Key

☐ represents 1 square unit

What is the area of Randall's desk top?

Answer: _____

3. Abbey shaded this design on grid paper.

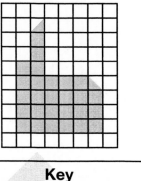

Key

☐ represents 1 square inch (in.²)

What is the area of Abbey's shaded design?

Answer: _____

4. Kendrick made this design for a banner in art class.

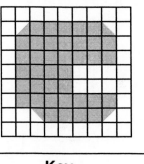

Key

☐ represents 1 square foot (ft.²)

What is the area of Kendrick's shaded design?

Answer: _____

You make this look easy!

Words for the Wise

area	square foot (ft.²)	square unit
square centimeter (cm²)	square inch (in.²)	square yard (yd.²)
	square meter (m²)	two-dimensional figure

partner practice

1. Nita shaded this symmetric design for art class.

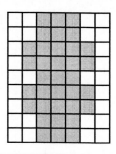

Key

□ represents 1 square centimeter (cm²)

What is the area of Nita's shaded design?

Ⓐ 81 cm²   Ⓒ 36 cm²

Ⓑ 66 cm²   Ⓓ 35 cm²

2. Muriel has a sheet of drawing paper divided into square inches.

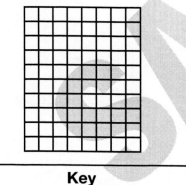

Key

□ represents 1 square inch (in.²)

What is the area of Muriel's paper?

Ⓐ 80 in.²   Ⓒ 58 in.²

Ⓑ 70 in.²   Ⓓ 36 in.²

3. Ollie made this quilt design.

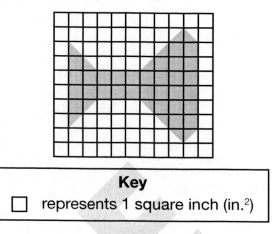

Key

□ represents 1 square inch (in.²)

What is the area of the shaded part of Ollie's design?

Ⓐ 31 in.²   Ⓒ 42 in.²

Ⓑ 36 in.²   Ⓓ 110 in.²

4. Look at Figure A and Figure B on this grid.

Key

□ represents 1 square unit

What is the difference between the areas of Figure A and Figure B?

Ⓐ 18 square units   Ⓒ 4 square units

Ⓑ 14 square units   Ⓓ 2 square units

               Level 3

1. The design shows the tile pattern in Gary's bathroom. The shaded part is blue and the unshaded part is white.

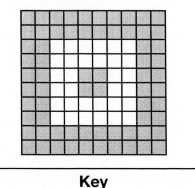

> **Key**
> ☐ represents 1 square inch (in.²)

What is the area of the white part of the design?

Ⓐ 32 in.²   Ⓒ 78 in.²

Ⓑ 36 in.²   Ⓓ 100 in.²

2. Rodolfo's chessboard is marked with black and white squares.

> **Key**
> ☐ represents 1 square inch (in.²)

What is the area of Rodolfo's chessboard?

Ⓐ 16 in.²   Ⓒ 36 in.²

Ⓑ 32 in.²   Ⓓ 64 in.²

3. Figure A and Figure B are shown in this diagram.

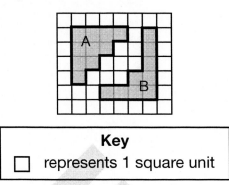

> **Key**
> ☐ represents 1 square unit

How much greater is the area of Figure A than the area of Figure B?

Ⓐ The figures have the same area.

Ⓑ 1 square unit

Ⓒ 9 square units

Ⓓ 10 square units

4. This is a diagram of a park. The shaded section represents a pool in the park.

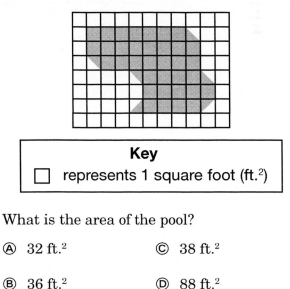

> **Key**
> ☐ represents 1 square foot (ft.²)

What is the area of the pool?

Ⓐ 32 ft.²   Ⓒ 38 ft.²

Ⓑ 36 ft.²   Ⓓ 88 ft.²

Name _____

1. Look at Figure A and Figure B on this grid.

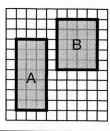

Key

☐ represents 1 square centimeter (cm²)

How much less is the area of Figure B than the area of Figure A?

Ⓐ 1 cm²

Ⓒ 18 cm²

Ⓑ 2 cm²

Ⓓ 20 cm²

2. This is a diagram of a school playground. The shaded section represents the grassy play area. The section **not** shaded is the concrete part of the playground.

Key

☐ represents 1 square meter (m²)

What is the area of the concrete part of the playground?

Ⓐ 61 m²

Ⓒ 51 m²

Ⓑ 52 m²

Ⓓ 19 m²

3. This design was used on the outside wall of the mall.

Key

☐ represents 1 square foot (ft.²)

What is the area of the part of the design that is **not** shaded?

Ⓐ 40 ft.²

Ⓒ 56 ft.²

Ⓑ 44 ft.²

Ⓓ 100 ft.²

4. Rocio drew this design.

Key

☐ represents 1 square inch (in.²)

What is the area of the shaded part of Rocio's design?

Ⓐ 80 in.²

Ⓒ 40 in.²

Ⓑ 43 in.²

Ⓓ 38 in.²

5. Look at the figures for questions 2 and 4. Explain how you were able to count square units when some of the squares were not completely shaded.

_____

_____

_____

 Level 3

Name _____

Analysis/Analyze

1. Ed uses 1-centimeter color tiles to build this rectangle. The area of the rectangle is 16 square centimeters. Ed doubles the length and the width of the rectangle. What is the area of the new rectangle?

Answer: _____

Explain how you found your answer.

_____
_____
_____

Synthesis/Create

2. Use this dot paper to create 3 different rectangles with an area of 24 square units each.

Journal: Analysis/Analyze

What is the difference between the area and the perimeter of a two-dimensional figure?

_____
_____
_____
_____
_____

★ **motivation station**

I'm in the Area

Use the centimeter grid paper below to play *I'm in the Area* with a partner. Partners need two number/dot cubes and one game board. Each player uses a different color crayon or marker. Player 1 rolls the cubes and adds or subtracts the two digits. The player then colors that number of squares on the game board. Colored squares must touch on a least one side. Play then passes to Player 2, who repeats the steps. If a player cannot color the indicated number of squares, he/she loses that turn. Play continues for 5 rounds. Each player then counts the total number of squares colored to determine his/her area. The player with the greatest area colored is the winner. NOTE: To use the game board for more than one game, players may use colored centimeter cubes to mark their areas.

Total area for Player 1: _____

Total area for Player 2: _____

┌─ **Parent Activities** ─────────────────────────────────┐

1. Provide your child with grid paper. Draw a basic design such as a rectangle. Have your child color the squares within the design and count to see how many squares are colored. Explain that the number of square units colored is the area of the design.

2. On grid paper, draw an irregular design with some of the squares divided in half diagonally. Have your child color the design and find the area. Show your child that 2 half-squares equal 1 whole square.

 Level 3

Name _____

1. For an art project, Audie is gluing multicolored square tiles on an art board to create a mosaic design. To determine how many square tiles he needs, Audie glues tiles along 2 of the sides as shown.

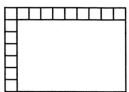

Explain how Audie can use this information to find the area of his design and determine the total number of tiles he needs for his project.

_____

_____

_____

2. Mr. Lopez is building a backyard playhouse for his daughter. The plans for the playhouse have the dimensions shown in this drawing.

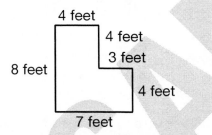

How can Mr. Lopez find the total area of the playhouse using the measurements on his floor plan?

_____

_____

What is the total area?

Answer: _____

3. Jessica made a quilt using fabric squares that measure 1 foot on each side. Jessica's quilt is shown in the picture.

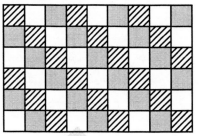

How many fabric pieces did Jessica use in her quilt?

Answer: _____

What are the dimensions of Jessica's quilt?

Length = _____ Width = _____

What is the total area of Jessica's quilt?

_____

How could you find the area of the quilt without counting the fabric squares?

Answer: _____

_____

4. The top part of the window in Steven's bedroom is covered by a window shade. The glass panes on the bottom part of the window are not covered. This diagram shows Steven's window.

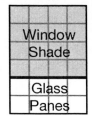

Find the total area of Steven's entire window. Show all work.

Answer: _____

You learned it correctly!

Words for the Wise

area	length	square inch (in.²)	
compose/decompose	square centimeter (cm²)	square meter (m²)	square yard (yd.²)
dimension	square foot / feet (ft.²)	square unit	width

★ **partner practice**

1. Mrs. Bonner's third-grade class is planning a vegetable garden. The garden will be a rectangle 8 feet long and 4 feet wide as shown.

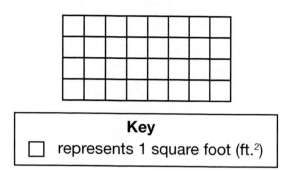

Key

☐ represents 1 square foot (ft.²)

The students need to find the area of the garden so they will know how much fertilizer to purchase to cover the soil. Which of the following does **not** describe a way the students can find the area, in square feet, of the garden?

Ⓐ They can multiply 4 × 8.

Ⓑ They can add 8 + 4 + 8 + 4.

Ⓒ They can add 8 + 8 + 8 + 8.

Ⓓ They can cover the garden plot with square foot tiles and count the tiles.

2. Which of the following rectangles has the smallest area?

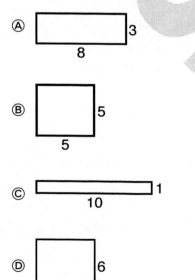

Ⓐ 8 by 3

Ⓑ 5 by 5

Ⓒ 10 by 1

Ⓓ 6 by 6

3. Coach Smith put up a volleyball net in the gym, dividing the room into two parts.

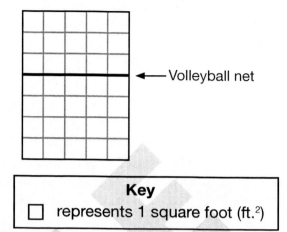

← Volleyball net

Key

☐ represents 1 square foot (ft.²)

The total area of the gym floor can be found from the areas of each part. Which expression can be used to find the area of the entire gym floor?

Ⓐ 3 + 5 + 4 + 5

Ⓑ (3 + 5) × (4 + 5)

Ⓒ (3 × 4) + (5 × 5)

Ⓓ (3 × 5) + (4 × 5)

4. Dennis wants to add a workshop to the side of his garage. The floor plan is shown.

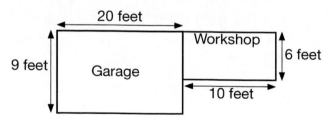

What will be the area, in square feet (ft.²), of the garage and the workshop?

Ⓐ 450 ft.²

Ⓑ 240 ft.²

Ⓒ 110 ft.²

Ⓓ 45 ft.²

 Level 3

Name _____

1. Nadia and her dad are building a sidewalk using square bricks placed inside a rectangular form. To find the number of bricks needed for each rectangle, Nadia decided to find the area by filling in one of the rectangles with bricks as shown.

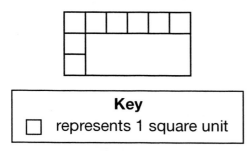

Key

☐ represents 1 square unit

Which statement shows the number of bricks Nadia would use in each rectangular form?

Ⓐ She would need 18 bricks because $6 \times 3 = 18$.

Ⓑ She would need 9 bricks because $6 + 3 = 9$.

Ⓒ She would need 3 bricks because $6 - 3 = 3$.

Ⓓ She would need 2 bricks because $6 \div 3 = 2$.

2. A teacher hung posters on a large wall in her classroom. She hung math posters in one area and science posters in the other area. The math area measured 42 square feet, and the science area measured 24 square feet.

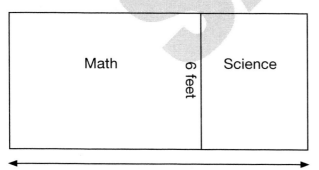

What is the length, in feet (ft.), of the wall?

Ⓐ 4 ft.   Ⓒ 8 ft.

Ⓑ 7 ft.   Ⓓ 11 ft.

3. Darnell's father wants to put a media room in their house. He plans to install a movie screen that will completely cover one wall of the media room. He measured the wall and found that its area is 72 square feet. Which of the following could be the dimensions, in feet (ft.), of the movie screen?

Ⓐ 9 ft. by 9 ft.

Ⓑ 10 ft. by 7 ft.

Ⓒ 9 ft. by 8 ft.

Ⓓ 20 ft. by 4 ft.

4. The Baldwin City Parks Department is planning a new public swimming pool. The pool will have a swimming area, a diving area, and a kiddie area as shown in the diagram.

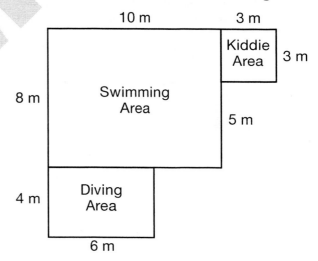

Which of these can be used to find the total area of the new swimming pool?

Ⓐ $(4 \times 6) + (8 \times 5) + (3 \times 3)$

Ⓑ $(10 \times 6) + (3 \times 8)$

Ⓒ $(3 \times 3) + (8 \times 10) + (6 \times 4)$

Ⓓ $(3 \times 3) \times (8 \times 10) \times (6 \times 4)$

★assessment

1. Megan tiled a rectangle with an area of 24 square centimeters. Which of these could **not** be Megan's rectangle?

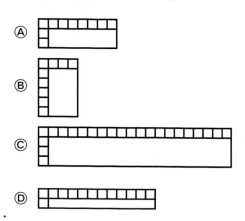

Ⓐ

Ⓑ

Ⓒ

Ⓓ

2. Diann wants to place her bookshelf and computer desk side-by-side in her bedroom. The gray section represents the bookshelf and the white section represents the computer desk in this model.

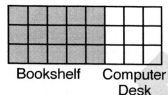

Bookshelf   Computer Desk

Which expression can be used to determine the amount of floor space Diann needs in her bedroom for both pieces of furniture?

Ⓐ 5 + 3 + 3 + 3   Ⓒ 15 × 9

Ⓑ (5 × 3) + (3 × 3)   Ⓓ (8 + 3) + (8 + 3)

3. Andrew needs a rectangular rug that covers at least 36 square feet in his office. Which could be the dimensions of the rug he buys?

Ⓐ 6 feet long and 3 feet wide

Ⓑ 8 feet long and 4 feet wide

Ⓒ 9 feet long and 2 feet wide

Ⓓ 9 feet long and 4 feet wide

4. Aaron and his brother, Thomas, were each building a scale model of an animal pen for their scout projects. Aaron's model measured 5 by 5 units, and Thomas' model measured 5 by 8 units. The large rectangle shows how the two pens were combined.

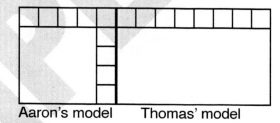

Aaron's model   Thomas' model

Which of the following could **not** be used to find the area in square units of the combined pens?

Ⓐ Multiply 5 × 5 and 5 × 8, and add the two products.

Ⓑ Add 5 + 8 and multiply the sum by 5.

Ⓒ Add 13 + 13 + 13 + 13 + 13.

Ⓓ Add 5 + 5 + 8 + 5.

5. Holt Elementary School is selling advertising space for the yearbook. The layout for the different rectangular ads on a page is shown in the diagram.

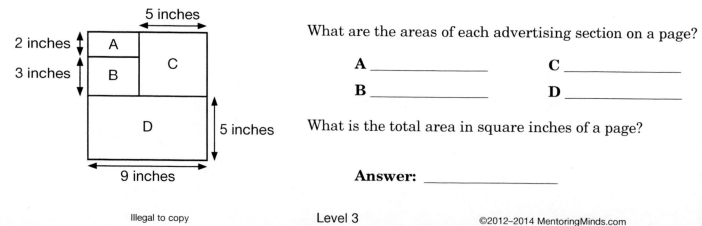

What are the areas of each advertising section on a page?

A _____   C _____

B _____   D _____

What is the total area in square inches of a page?

Answer: _____

       Level 3

Analysis/Analyze

1. One square foot of garden space can contain 6 bean plants, 7 lettuce plants, 8 radish plants or 1 tomato plant. How many square feet of garden space would be needed for each of the following:

42 bean plants _____   28 lettuce plants _____

40 radish plants _____   8 tomato plants _____

What is the total area, in square feet, needed for this garden?

Answer: _____

Use the grid paper to draw one possible model of this garden.

Analysis/Analyze

2. Nate was hired to lay new tile floors in Mrs. Walker's kitchen, hall, and laundry room. Nate measured the dimensions of each room and recorded the measurements on a floor plan as shown. As he began to calculate the area of each room, he accidentally spilled a cup of coffee on his plan.

23 ft

Hall   3 ft   Laundry Room   6 ft

10 ft.   Kitchen   10 ft

7 ft   4 ft.

9 ft

How can Nate determine the number of square feet of tile he needs to lay in Mrs. Walker's house?

_____

_____

_____

Journal: Analysis/Analyze

Quince wanted to calculate the total area of his bedroom and closet. He drew a model on grid paper. Quince knew he could find the total area of the bedroom and closet by first finding the areas of each space and adding them together. Describe a way that Quince could find the total area of his bedroom and closet by using subtraction.

_____

_____

_____

_____

Bedroom   Closet

☐ represents 1 square foot

★ motivation station

Hooray! Arrays!

Play *Hooray! Arrays!* with a partner. Each player needs the game sheet below. Each pair of players needs two number/dot cubes. In Round 1, players each roll the number cubes to determine the dimensions of a rectangular array. Each player uses color tiles to create a model of the rectangle and sketches the rectangle in the Round 1 box. Players record the addition and multiplication number sentences that describe the arrays. A player's score for each round is the area of the rectangle. Play continues for four rounds. The player with the highest total score for four rounds is the winner.

Round 1	Round 2
Addition sentence _____ Multiplication sentence_____ Score _____	Addition sentence _____ Multiplication sentence_____ Score _____
Round 3	Round 4
Addition sentence _____ Multiplication sentence_____ Score _____	Addition sentence _____ Multiplication sentence_____ Score _____

Parent Activities

1. For a snack, arrange square crackers (e.g., Wheat Thins®, Cheez-Its®, etc.) as shown. Ask your child to determine the area if the rectangle was complete. Then, use more crackers to complete the rectangle and check the answer. Point out that the area of the rectangle can be calculated by multiplying length × width.

2. Help your child measure the length and width of his/her bedroom to the nearest foot. Calculate the area in square feet by multiplying the dimensions. Then, measure the length and width of furniture to the nearest foot. Have your child multiply the length and the width to determine the area of floor space, in square feet, occupied by each piece of furniture. Find the total floor area covered by the furniture. Record on grid paper or graph paper, using the scale 1 square represents 1 square foot. Extend the activity by having your child determine how many square feet are **not** occupied by furniture.

 Level 3

Name _____

1. Look at the figure outlined on this square grid.

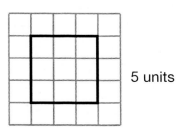

5 units

What is the perimeter of the figure on the grid?

Answer: _____

2. This figure is a quadrilateral with sides measured in centimeters.

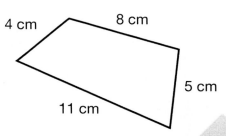

Write an equation that shows the perimeter of the quadrilateral.

_____

3. Mr. Trevino drew this diagram of his garden.

8 feet

13 feet

How many feet of fencing does Mr. Trevino need to fence his garden?

Answer: _____

4. The perimeter of the eraser is 26 centimeters.

5 cm

What is the length of the eraser? Show your work.

Answer: _____

5. Ye Olde Cake Shoppe has two different boxes for packaging cookies. The outline of the bottom of each box is shown.

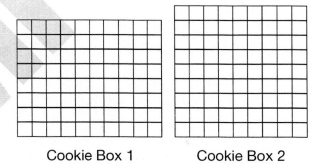

Cookie Box 1   Cookie Box 2

Which box has the greater perimeter?

Answer: _____

Which box has the greater area?

Answer: _____

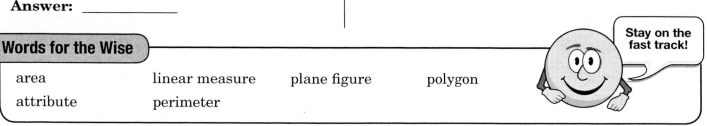

Words for the Wise

area	linear measure	plane figure	polygon
attribute	perimeter		

Stay on the fast track!

partner practice

1. Use a centimeter ruler to measure the perimeter of this polygon. Measure to the nearest centimeter.

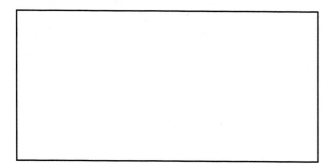

What is the perimeter of this polygon?

Ⓐ 24 cm

Ⓑ 12 cm

Ⓒ 8 cm

Ⓓ 4 cm

2. Look at the plane figures on this grid.

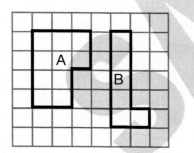

Which of the following is a true statement about the two figures?

Ⓐ The two figures have the same areas and same perimeters.

Ⓑ The two figures have the same areas but different perimeters.

Ⓒ The two figures have the same perimeters but different areas.

Ⓓ The two figures have different areas and different perimeters.

3. The base of Pam's bug container is shaped like a rectangle.

14 cm

The length of the container is twice the width. What is the perimeter, in centimeters, of the bug container base?

Ⓐ 28 cm   Ⓒ 56 cm

Ⓑ 42 cm   Ⓓ 84 cm

4. The top of the teacher's desk is in the shape of a rectangle. It is **36** inches wide and **48** inches long.

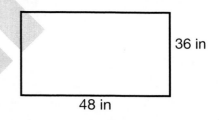

36 in

48 in

What is the perimeter of the desk top?

Ⓐ 186 in   Ⓒ 84 in

Ⓑ 168 in   Ⓓ 48 in

5. This figure has a perimeter of 19 inches.

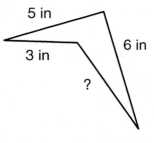

5 in
3 in
6 in
?

What is the missing length?

Ⓐ 8 in   Ⓒ 6 in

Ⓑ 7 in   Ⓓ 5 in

Level 3   ©2012–2014 MentoringMinds.com

Name _____

1. Look at Figure A and Figure B on this grid.

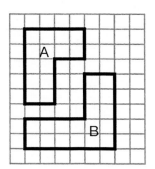

What is the difference between the perimeters of Figure A and Figure B?

Ⓐ 22 units

Ⓑ 18 units

Ⓒ 4 units

Ⓓ 2 units

2. Mrs. Jones and Mr. Reese each have a garden in their yards. Their gardens, measured in meters, are shown in this diagram.

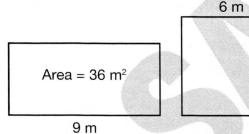

Mrs. Jones' Garden   Mr. Reese's Garden

Which statement about the two gardens is **not** true?

Ⓐ Mrs. Jones' garden has a width of 4 meters.

Ⓑ Mr. Reese's garden has a perimeter of 24 meters.

Ⓒ The two gardens have the same areas but different perimeters.

Ⓓ The two gardens have the same areas and perimeters.

3. The floor of Mr. Ables' garage is shaped like a rectangle.

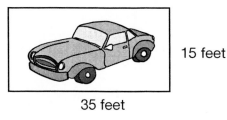

What is the perimeter, in feet, of the garage floor?

Ⓐ 50 ft   Ⓒ 140 ft

Ⓑ 100 ft   Ⓓ 150 ft

4. Hector wants to put chalk lines around the soccer field. Hector knows the perimeter of the soccer field is 300 yards.

P = 100 yd

What is the width of the soccer field?

Ⓐ 200 yd   Ⓒ 50 yd

Ⓑ 100 yd   Ⓓ 25 yd

5. What is the perimeter, in inches, of this figure?

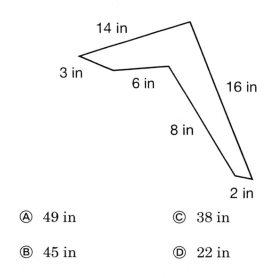

Ⓐ 49 in   Ⓒ 38 in

Ⓑ 45 in   Ⓓ 22 in

★ assessment

1. Use a centimeter ruler to measure the sides of this quadrilateral. Measure to the nearest centimeter.

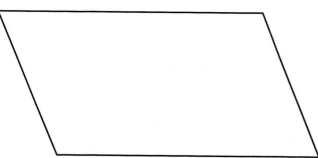

What is the perimeter of this quadrilateral?

Ⓐ 30 cm   Ⓒ 22 cm

Ⓑ 24 cm   Ⓓ 11 cm

2. Mr. Martin put lights around a rectangular window of his house.

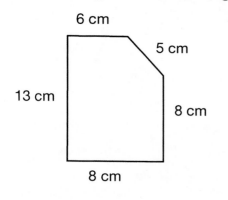

6 ft

Mr. Martin used 32 feet of lights. What is the length of Mr. Martin's window?

Ⓐ 5 ft   Ⓒ 12 ft

Ⓑ 10 ft   Ⓓ 20 ft

3. Cyndi has a sheet of 1-inch square stickers. Her sheet of stickers has 6 rows of 5 stickers as shown. If Cyndi tears off the bottom 2 rows of stickers and gives them to her brother, what is the new perimeter of her sheet of stickers?

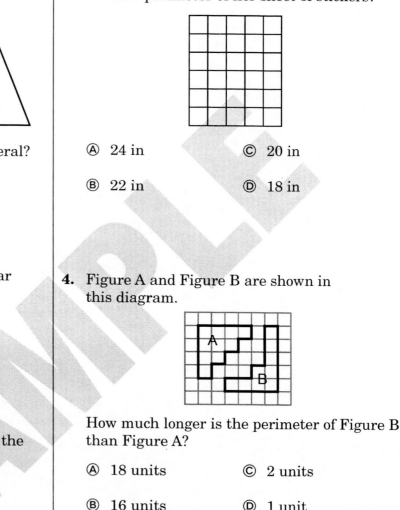

Ⓐ 24 in   Ⓒ 20 in

Ⓑ 22 in   Ⓓ 18 in

4. Figure A and Figure B are shown in this diagram.

How much longer is the perimeter of Figure B than Figure A?

Ⓐ 18 units   Ⓒ 2 units

Ⓑ 16 units   Ⓓ 1 unit

5. What is the perimeter of this figure? Show your work.

6 cm
5 cm
13 cm
8 cm
8 cm

Answer: _____

Name _____

Analysis/Analyze

1. Sally and Jon planted a flower garden in their back yard. Their garden is shown in this diagram. They want to put a fence around the garden. How many feet of fencing do Sally and Jon need to purchase?

Answer: _____

Explain how you found your answer.

_____

_____

_____

11 ft

3 ft

?

?

10 ft

4 ft

Analysis/Analyze

2. Greg's painting is shaped like a rectangle and has a perimeter of 36 inches. In the space below, draw at least three different rectangles that could represent Greg's painting. Label the length and width of each rectangular painting. Record the area of each painting inside the rectangle.

What conclusion can you make about areas and perimeters? _____

_____

Journal: Application/Apply

If you know the perimeter of a polygon but are missing the measure of one side, how can you find the missing measure?

_____

_____

_____

_____

_____

Pattern Block Perimeters

Play *Pattern Block Perimeters* with a partner. Each pair needs a set of pattern blocks (use only yellow hexagons, red trapezoids, blue rhombuses, and green triangles), a game sheet with the pattern block spinner, and a pencil and paper clip or hair pin for the spinner. Before starting the game, players should look closely at the pattern blocks. Each side of the hexagon, the triangle, and the rhombus is 1 inch long. The long side of the trapezoid is 2 inches long, and the remaining sides of the trapezoid are 1 inch long.

Player 1 spins the pattern block spinner, selects the pattern block shown, sets it on the table, and states the perimeter of the block. If player 1 states the correct perimeter, he/she keeps the block for the next turn. If player 1 states an incorrect perimeter, the block goes back to the pile. Player 2 repeats these steps for his/her turn. In the second round, player 1 spins again, selects that pattern block, and adds it to the original pattern block with two sides touching to form a larger polygon. Player 1 states the perimeter of the combined structure of blocks. If correct, player 1 keeps both blocks, but cannot move the position of either block. If incorrect, the block from round 2 is returned to the pile. Play continues in this manner until one player's structure reaches a perimeter of 30 inches or more, and the player is declared the winner.

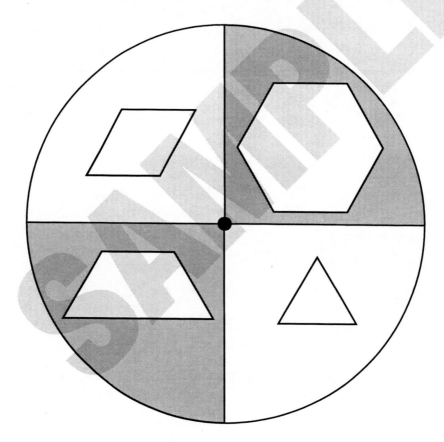

Parent Activities

1. Help your child find the perimeter of a flower bed, patio, or floor of a room by measuring around the space and adding the measurements.

2. Talk to your child about situations that might require finding perimeter (e.g., building a fence, framing a picture).

 Level 3

1. Name a polygon that has 2 more sides than a hexagon.

   Answer: _____

   Draw a picture to support your answer.

4. Draw the shapes that are missing in this pattern of polygons.

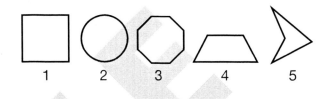

2. Write the numbers of the figures that are polygons.

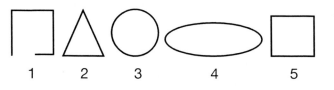

   Answer: _____

   Explain your answer.

   _____

   _____

5. Write the numbers of the figures that are **not** quadrilaterals.

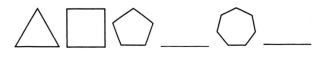

   Answer: _____

   Explain your answer.

   _____

   _____

3. Study the figures shown.

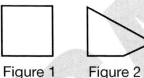

   Name one way the two figures are alike.

   Answer: _____

   _____

   Name one way the two figures are different.

   Answer: _____

   _____

6. Parallelograms are quadrilaterals that have two pairs of parallel sides. The opposite sides are equal in length. Is a rectangle a parallelogram?

   Answer: _____

   Is a square a parallelogram?

   Answer: _____

   How do you know?

   _____

   _____

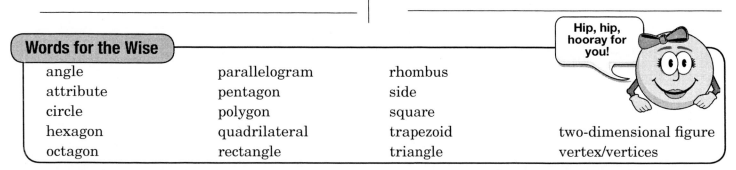

Words for the Wise

angle	parallelogram	rhombus
attribute	pentagon	side
circle	polygon	square
hexagon	quadrilateral	trapezoid
octagon	rectangle	triangle

two-dimensional figure
vertex/vertices

Hip, hip, hooray for you!

partner practice

1. Dominic drew these six figures.

Which of the following best describes these figures?

Ⓐ three-dimensional figures

Ⓑ polygons

Ⓒ quadrilaterals

Ⓓ triangles

2. Which of these figures have more sides than a quadrilateral?

Ⓐ circles and triangles

Ⓑ pentagons and squares

Ⓒ pentagons and octagons

Ⓓ parallelograms and trapezoids

3. A soccer ball has a pattern made of two different polygons as shown in this figure.

What two shapes are shown on a soccer ball?

Ⓐ hexagon and trapezoid

Ⓑ pentagon and octagon

Ⓒ pentagon and hexagon

Ⓓ hexagon and octagon

4. Lucy thought of a mystery shape. She gave her friend these clues to help her guess the shape.

• It is a two-dimensional shape.

• It has an even number of sides.

• It has 3 pairs of parallel sides.

Which could be Lucy's mystery shape?

Ⓐ triangle   Ⓒ square

Ⓑ hexagon   Ⓓ parallelogram

5. Which polygon has fewer sides than a rectangle?

Ⓐ triangle

Ⓑ square

Ⓒ hexagon

Ⓓ octagon

6. Raymond took photographs of the street signs near his house.

Which of the attributes do **not** describe Raymond's figures?

Ⓐ All the signs are parallelograms.

Ⓑ All the signs are squares.

Ⓒ All the signs are quadrilaterals.

Ⓓ All the signs are polygons.

1. Yolanda drew this irregular polygon in her journal.

Based on the attributes of this figure, what is the name of this irregular polygon?

Ⓐ quadrilateral

Ⓑ pentagon

Ⓒ hexagon

Ⓓ octagon

2. Mrs. Dover drew this shape on the board.

Leonardo said, "That shape is an octagon." Was Leonardo correct? How do you know?

Ⓐ Yes, it is a closed figure with 8 sides.

Ⓑ No, it is a hexagon.

Ⓒ No, it does not look like a stop sign.

Ⓓ Yes, it can be divided into a square and 4 triangles.

3. Which geometric shape best represents the shaded face of this figure?

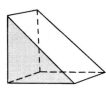

Ⓐ pentagon   Ⓒ square

Ⓑ rectangle   Ⓓ triangle

4. The teacher drew a figure on the board and asked John to explain why the figure is **not** a quadrilateral.

Which of these should be John's answer?

Ⓐ The figure does not have two parallel sides.

Ⓑ The figure does not have four sides of equal measure.

Ⓒ The figure is not a closed figure.

Ⓓ The figure does not have four straight sides.

5. Study these shapes.

Which is the best description for the 3 shapes?

Ⓐ polygons with parallel sides

Ⓑ polygons with fewer than 7 sides

Ⓒ polygons with fewer than 6 sides

Ⓓ polygons with square corners

6. Taylor sorted 6 shapes in two groups based on an attribute.

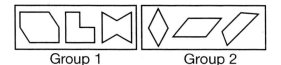

Group 1   Group 2

What labels could Taylor put on the two groups?

Ⓐ Hexagons and Pentagons

Ⓑ Octagons and Trapezoids

Ⓒ Hexagons and Quadrilaterals

Ⓓ Quadrilaterals and Parallelograms

★assessment

1. Ian made a mobile using only hexagonal cutout shapes. Which figures could **not** be used on Ian's mobile?

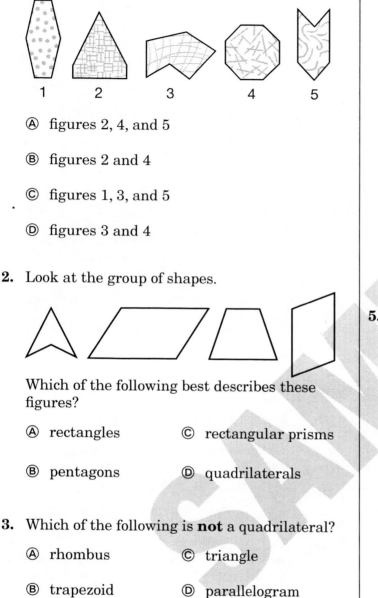

    1   2   3   4   5

   Ⓐ figures 2, 4, and 5

   Ⓑ figures 2 and 4

   Ⓒ figures 1, 3, and 5

   Ⓓ figures 3 and 4

2. Look at the group of shapes.

   Which of the following best describes these figures?

   Ⓐ rectangles   Ⓒ rectangular prisms

   Ⓑ pentagons   Ⓓ quadrilaterals

3. Which of the following is **not** a quadrilateral?

   Ⓐ rhombus   Ⓒ triangle

   Ⓑ trapezoid   Ⓓ parallelogram

4. While riding to school with his mother, Paul noticed that these traffic signs shared some of the same attributes.

   What attribute do all the signs share?

   Ⓐ The signs are all triangles.

   Ⓑ The signs are all quadrilaterals.

   Ⓒ The signs are all parallelograms.

   Ⓓ The signs are all polygons.

5. Kara read this math riddle in her *Kids World* magazine.

• I am a polygon.
• I am a quadrilateral.
• I am a parallelogram with four square corners.
What am I?

   Which figure was described by the riddle?

6. Ernie drew a square and then drew some line segments in the square as shown.

   Using different colors of markers or pencils, trace and name at least 4 different polygons you can find in Ernie's figure.

   _____

   _____

   _____

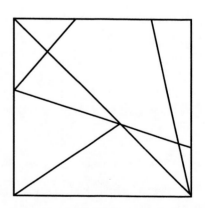

     Level 3

Name _____

Application/Apply

1. Macy drew a snowman made of geometric figures. How many quadrilaterals did Macy use in her picture?

Answer: _____

Name three different quadrilaterals Macy used in her picture.

_____

_____

_____

Analysis/Analyze

2. Use common attributes to classify quadrilaterals on this Venn diagram. Write the name of each quadrilateral in the correct region, then draw an example. Use these words as the labels: rectangle, square, quadrilateral, parallelogram, rhombus.

Journal: Analysis/Analyze

Are all trapezoids members of the quadrilateral family?

Answer: _____

Are all quadrilaterals members of the trapezoid family?

Answer: _____

Explain your answers with words and pictures.

_____

_____

_____

Name _____

Figure It Out!

On the grid below, use a different color marker or colored pencil to outline and shade the figures named. Color the key to show which colors you used for each shaded figure.

1. triangle
2. rectangle
3. parallelogram that is **not** a rectangle
4. trapezoid
5. different shaped trapezoid

6. pentagon
7. hexagon
8. heptagon
9. octagon
10. rhombus

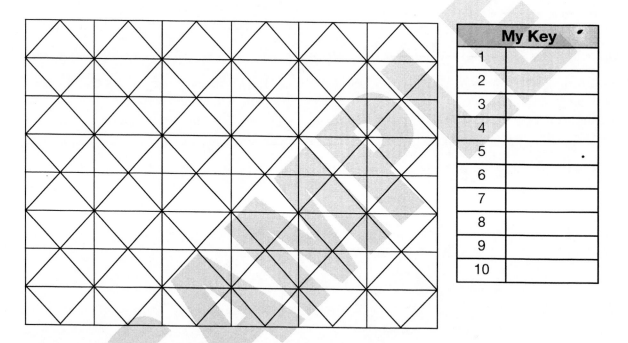

My Key	
1	
2	
3	
4	
5	
6	
7	
8	
9	
10	

Parent Activities

1. Play "I Spy" with your child. Locate a two-dimensional shape and give your child clues, such as, "I spy a quadrilateral in the kitchen." As your child guesses the shapes, ask him/her to explain what attributes help solve the riddle.

2. Look for quadrilaterals around your house. Make a list of the items. Then, see if your child can organize them by categories (e.g., square, rectangle, rhombus, trapezoid).

3. Use mini-marshmallows and toothpicks or stir straws to create a variety of two-dimensional shapes. Compare and contrast the different attributes of the shapes. As an extension, change the size of the figure or use different angles to create unusual examples of a given shape.

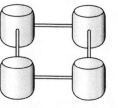

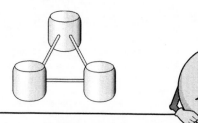

 Level 3

1. Mrs. Kalifa gave her students geometric figures and asked them to partition the shapes into equal areas. Selena and Robert both described the shaded part of their trapezoids as $\frac{1}{3}$ of the area of the trapezoid.

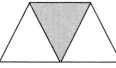

Selena's Model   Robert's Model

Are both students correct?

Answer: _____

Explain your reasoning.

_____

_____

2. Courtney divided a square into congruent triangles by drawing two diagonals across the square, connecting each pair of opposite corners. Draw Courtney's figure.

How many triangles were formed?

Answer: _____

If Courtney shades two opposite triangles that touch only at a vertex, what fraction of the square is shaded?

Answer: _____

3. Draw lines to partition this figure into eight equal parts.

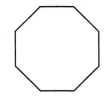

Shade one part. What fraction represents the shaded part of the figure?

Answer: _____

4. Mary said that the unshaded part of this hexagon represents $\frac{2}{4}$ of the hexagon's area. Is Mary correct?

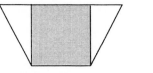

Answer: _____

Explain your answer.

_____

_____

5. Delia, Hector, and Robert each made a pan of fudge for the class candy sale. They used identical square pans and cut the pans of fudge into eight equal parts. Each student cut the fudge into eight parts in a different way. Show how the students might have cut the fudge differently into eight equal parts.

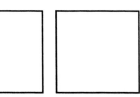

Words for the Wise

area	fraction	partition	whole
denominator	numerator		

You're sensational!

★ partner practice

1. These patterns can be folded to create pyramids. Which pyramid pattern has been divided so that all parts have equal areas?

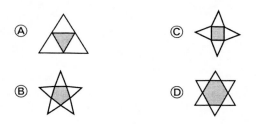

Ⓐ   Ⓒ

Ⓑ   Ⓓ

2. This figure has been divided into equal parts.

What fraction of the total area of the figure is shaded?

Ⓐ $\frac{2}{6}$ Ⓒ $\frac{1}{6}$

Ⓑ $\frac{2}{8}$ Ⓓ $\frac{1}{8}$

3. Chef Lang created his famous 7-layer chocolate delight for a cooking contest. He divided the dessert into rectangles with equal areas as shown.

What fraction of the figure is the shaded rectangle?

Ⓐ $\frac{1}{2}$ Ⓒ $\frac{1}{4}$

Ⓑ $\frac{1}{3}$ Ⓓ $\frac{1}{5}$

4. Mrs. Farr purchased a hexagonal bathroom rug with a total area of 21 square feet. The rug was divided into three sections with equal areas.

Which of the following is **not** a true statement about Mrs. Farr's bathroom rug?

Ⓐ Mrs. Farr's rug is divided into thirds.

Ⓑ The area of the white section of Mrs. Farr's rug is 7 square feet.

Ⓒ The area of the black section of Mrs. Farr's rug is 3 square feet.

Ⓓ The gray and black sections of Mrs. Farr's rug represent $\frac{2}{3}$ of the total area of the rug.

5. Lexie divided these hexagons into two parts and shaded one part.

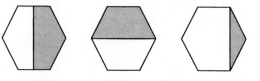

Which shaded parts represent $\frac{1}{2}$ of the area of the hexagon?

Ⓐ only the shaded trapezoid

Ⓑ both the shaded triangle and the shaded pentagon

Ⓒ only the shaded pentagon

Ⓓ both the shaded trapezoid and the shaded pentagon

 Level 3 ©2012–2014 MentoringMinds.com

1. Which of these figures does **not** have $\frac{3}{6}$ of its area shaded?

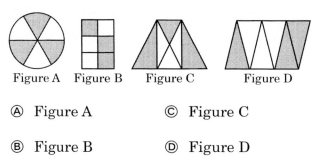

Figure A   Figure B   Figure C   Figure D

Ⓐ Figure A   Ⓒ Figure C

Ⓑ Figure B   Ⓓ Figure D

2. A net is a pattern made of two-dimensional shapes that can be folded to create a three-dimensional shape. Which net is divided so that all parts have equal areas?

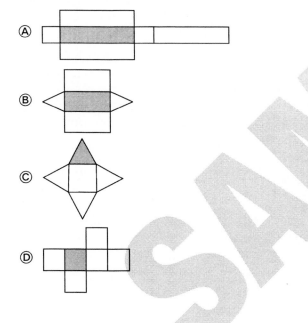

3. John divided a parallelogram into four triangles with equal areas.

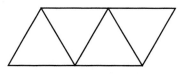

What fraction of the parallelogram's area would one triangle represent?

Ⓐ $\frac{1}{4}$ Ⓒ $\frac{3}{4}$

Ⓑ $\frac{1}{3}$ Ⓓ $\frac{4}{4}$

4. Farmer Dell's farm is triangular in shape. He divides his farm into 4 identical sections. Farmer Dell and his three sons each plant a crop in one section as shown. The total area of the farm is 36 acres. Which statement about the farm is **not** true?

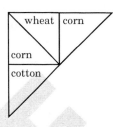

Ⓐ Each person plants crops on $\frac{1}{4}$ of the land.

Ⓑ The two sections that form a square have a greater area than the other two sections combined.

Ⓒ Each section of the farm has an area of 9 acres.

Ⓓ The area planted in corn is equal to $\frac{2}{4}$ of the area of the farm.

5. Kason drew these four shapes. Which figure does **not** have $\frac{1}{2}$ of its total area shaded?

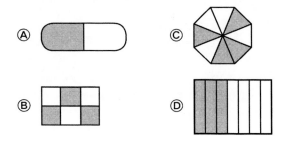

6. Jodi drew a hopscotch board on the sidewalk using identical squares. Jodi skipped over the shaded squares. What fraction of the total area of the board did Jodi skip over?

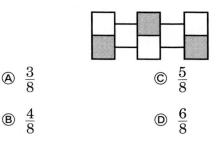

Ⓐ $\frac{3}{8}$ Ⓒ $\frac{5}{8}$

Ⓑ $\frac{4}{8}$ Ⓓ $\frac{6}{8}$

★ assessment

1. The shaded part appears to be —

- Ⓐ $\frac{1}{4}$ of the area of the trapezoid

- Ⓑ $\frac{1}{4}$ of the area of the hexagon

- Ⓒ $\frac{1}{3}$ of the area of the hexagon

- Ⓓ $\frac{3}{4}$ of the area of the trapezoid

2. Cheryl drew four polygons. Then she drew line segments connecting the center of each polygon to the vertices of the polygon.

What does the fraction representing the shaded area of each polygon have in common with the number of sides?

- Ⓐ The number of sides on each polygon is the denominator in each fraction.

- Ⓑ The number of sides on each polygon is the numerator in each fraction.

- Ⓒ The number of sides on each polygon is the sum of the numerator and denominator.

- Ⓓ The number of sides on each polygon is the difference between the denominator and the numerator.

3. Leo used color tiles to create a rectangle as shown.

What fraction of the rectangle's area is represented by the shaded tile?

- Ⓐ $\frac{1}{4}$
- Ⓒ $\frac{5}{6}$
- Ⓑ $\frac{1}{6}$
- Ⓓ $\frac{3}{4}$

4. The Claude family wants to build a dog pen for their dog. The pen will be L-shaped as shown. The pen will have two equal areas, one with gravel and the other planted with grass.

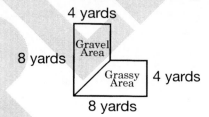

The total area of the dog pen is 48 square yards. Which of these is a true statement about the dog pen?

- Ⓐ The grassy area is larger than the gravel area.

- Ⓑ The area of the dog pen can be calculated by multiplying 8×8.

- Ⓒ The dog pen is divided into two halves.

- Ⓓ Each section of the dog pen is rectangular.

5. Divide each of these shapes into 6 equal parts. Then shade one part to represent $\frac{1}{6}$ of the whole.

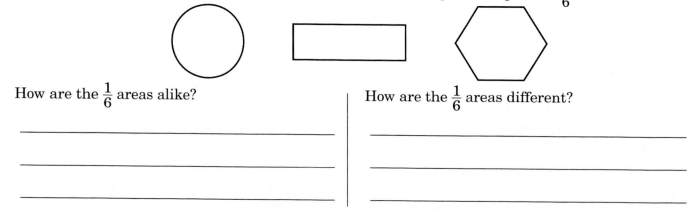

How are the $\frac{1}{6}$ areas alike?

_____

_____

_____

How are the $\frac{1}{6}$ areas different?

_____

_____

_____

Name _____

Analysis/Analyze

1. Mrs. Jones has 20 students in her class. Her classroom has a bulletin board that is 5 feet tall and 8 feet long. She gave each student a sheet of drawing paper that measures exactly one square foot and asked them to draw a picture of a pet. Mrs. Jones put all the pet pictures on the bulletin board. No picture overlaps any other picture. Draw an example of how the bulletin board might look using shaded squares for each of the students' pictures.

What fraction of the bulletin board will be covered by pictures?

Answer: _____

Analysis/Analyze

2. The figure shown is a rectangle. How many different ways can this figure be partitioned to show sixths?

Use this space to justify your answer using pictures and words.

_____

_____

_____

Journal: Analysis/Analyze

Complete and explain the analogy shown in this picture.

is related to ____ the same way that _____ is related to

_____

_____

_____

_____

Honeycomb Nim

Play *Honeycomb Nim* with a partner using pattern blocks and one game board. Players take turns placing green triangles, blue parallelograms, red trapezoids, and yellow hexagons on the honeycomb. The person who places the block that covers the last empty space loses the game.

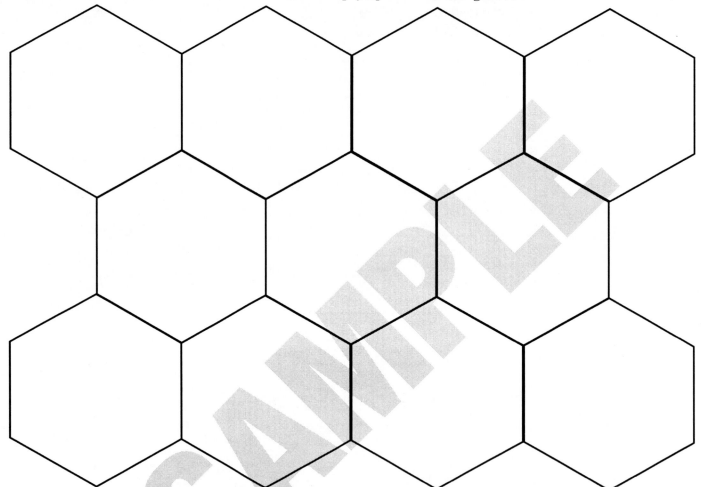

Answer the following questions:

1. The green triangle represents what fraction of the area of the yellow hexagon? _____

2. The blue parallelogram represents what fraction of the area of the yellow hexagon? _____

3. The red trapezoid represents what fraction of the area of the yellow hexagon? _____

Parent Activities

1. Use paper plates to explore different ways to divide circles into equal parts. Once your child has successfully divided the plate into equal areas, place any healthy snack into one or more of the equal parts. Then have your child tell you what fraction of his plate contains food. Help your child divide a circle into halves, thirds, fourths, sixths, and eighths.

2. Line up 2 dominoes, face down, to form a larger rectangle. Have your child turn over one domino and write a fraction for the rectangular area represented by the face-up domino. Repeat with 3, 4, 6, or 8 dominoes. Always turn over one domino in each larger rectangle, and record the fraction of the total area represented.

Notes

CHART YOUR SUCCESS

Color Mike or Molly *green* if your answer was correct or *red* if your answer was incorrect.

	Question 1	Question 2	Question 3	Question 4	Question 5	Question 6	Question 7	Total Right	Total Possible
Page 10 (3.OA.1) Interpret Products	☺	☺	☺	☺	☺				/5
Page 16 (3.OA.2) Interpret Quotients	☺	☺	☺	☺	☺				/5
Page 22 (3.OA.3) Solve Problems: ×/÷	☺	☺	☺	☺	☺	☺			/6
Page 28 (3.OA.4) Find Unknown: ×/÷	☺	☺	☺	☺	☺				/5
Page 34 (3.OA.5) Properties of Operations	☺	☺	☺	☺	☺	☺			/6
Page 40 (3.OA.6) Division as Unknown Factor	☺	☺	☺	☺	☺	☺			/6
Page 46 (3.OA.7) Use Strategies: ×/÷	☺	☺	☺	☺	☺	☺			/6
Page 52 (3.OA.8) Solve Problems: 2-step	☺	☺	☺	☺	☺				/5
Page 58 (3.OA.9) Identify Patterns	☺	☺	☺	☺	☺				/5
Page 64 (3.NBT.1) Round Numbers	☺	☺	☺	☺	☺	☺	☺		/7
Page 70 (3.NBT.2) Add/Subtract within 1000	☺	☺	☺	☺	☺	☺			/6
Page 76 (3.NBT.3) Multiply: 1-digit × 10s	☺	☺	☺	☺	☺	☺			/6
Page 82 (3.NF.1) Meaning of Fractions	☺	☺	☺	☺	☺	☺			/6

 Level 3

CHART YOUR SUCCESS

Color Mike or Molly **green** if your answer was correct or **red** if your answer was incorrect.

	Question 1	Question 2	Question 3	Question 4	Question 5	Question 6	Question 7	Total Right	Total Possible
Page 88 (3.NF.2) Fractions on a Number Line	🙂	🙂	🙂	🙂	🙂				/5
Page 94 (3.NF.3a-c) Equivalent Fractions	🙂	🙂	🙂	🙂	🙂				/5
Page 100 (3.NF.3d) Compare Fractions	🙂	🙂	🙂	🙂	🙂	🙂			/6
Page 106 (3.MD.1) Time	🙂	🙂	🙂	🙂	🙂				/5
Page 112 (3.MD.2) Liquid Volume/Mass	🙂	🙂	🙂	🙂	🙂	🙂			/6
Page 118 (3.MD.3) Graphs: Picture/Bar	🙂	🙂	🙂	🙂					/4
Page 124 (3.MD.4) Line Plots	🙂	🙂	🙂	🙂					/4
Page 130 (3.MD.5) Understand Area	🙂	🙂	🙂	🙂	🙂				/5
Page 136 (3.MD.6) Counting Square Units	🙂	🙂	🙂	🙂	🙂				/5
Page 142 (3.MD.7) Relate Area to ×/÷	🙂	🙂	🙂	🙂	🙂				/5
Page 148 (3.MD.8) Perimeter	🙂	🙂	🙂	🙂	🙂				/5
Page 154 (3.G.1) Classify 2-D Shapes	🙂	🙂	🙂	🙂	🙂	🙂			/6
Page 160 (3.G.2) Partition Shapes	🙂	🙂	🙂	🙂	🙂				/5

   Level 3

Math Glossary

A

addends - numbers that are added

addition - the operation of combining groups to find the total amount

a.m. - before noon; the time between 12 midnight and 12 noon

analog clock - a clock with a minute hand and an hour hand

angle - the figure formed by 2 rays that extend from a common endpoint

approximate - (*verb*) to find a result that is close to the exact answer; (*adj.*) close or near to the exact answer

area - the number of square units needed to cover a surface

array - an arrangement of objects in equal rows and columns

associative property of addition - a property of addition which states that the grouping of the addends does not change the sum
$$(1 + 2) + 3 = 1 + (2 + 3)$$

associative property of multiplication - a property of multiplication which states that the grouping of the factors does not change the product
$$(1 \times 2) \times 3 = 1 \times (2 \times 3)$$

attribute - a characteristic or property of a shape or thing

B

bar graph - a graph that uses horizontal or vertical bars to represent data

C

capacity - a measure of the amount of liquid a container will hold

chart - a diagram that illustrates information in the form of a table, graph, or picture

circle - a flat, round shape; all points on the edge of a circle are the same distance from the center

commutative property of addition - a property of addition which states that the sum stays the same when the order of the addends is changed
$$3 + 4 = 4 + 3$$

commutative property of multiplication - a property of multiplication which states that the product stays the same when the order of the factors is changed
$$2 \times 6 = 6 \times 2$$

compatible numbers - pairs of numbers that can easily be computed mentally; $23 + 27$ is close to $25 + 25$, so the estimate is 50.
$3720 \div 6$ is close to $3600 \div 6$, so the estimate is 600.

compose - to join numbers to create tens, hundreds, thousands, etc.; to join or put together parts to create a whole

D

data - a collection of facts gathered by observation, questioning, or measuring

decompose - to break down or break apart into smaller parts

denominator - the bottom number in a fraction; the total number of equal parts

difference - the answer to a subtraction problem

digit - one of the symbols 0, 1, 2, 3, 4, 5, 6, 7, 8, and 9 used to write numbers

digital clock - a clock that shows time in numbers

dimension - a measure in one direction; the length, width, or height of a figure

distributive property - multiplying a number by a sum is the same as multiplying the number by each addend of the sum and then adding the products
$2 \times (3 + 4) = (2 \times 3) + (2 \times 4)$

divide - to separate into equal groups

dividend - the number to be divided in a division problem

division - the operation of making equal groups to find the number in each group or to find the number of equal groups

divisor - the number by which a number is divided

E

eighth - one of eight equal parts in a whole

elapsed time - the amount of time that passes from the start of an activity to the end of that activity

equal parts - parts of a whole that are the same size

equal sign ($=$) - the symbol used to show that two sets or expressions are exactly the same in amount or value

equation - a number sentence that uses the equal sign to show that two amounts are equal

equivalent fractions - two or more fractions that are equal

estimate - (*noun*) an answer that is close to the exact answer ($42 + 61 \approx 100$, so 100 is the estimate of 42 and 61.) (*verb*) to guess about

even number - a whole number that ends with 0, 2, 4, 6, or 8; all even numbers have 2 as a factor

expanded form - a way to write numbers that shows the value of each digit

expression - a mathematical combination of numbers, operations, and variables

F

fact family - a set of related number sentences

factor - a number that is multiplied by another number to find a product

fourth - one of four equal parts in a whole

fraction - a number that names a part of a whole or part of a group

fraction bar - the horizontal line that separates the numerator from the denominator in a fraction

G

gram (g) - a metric unit used to measure mass

greater than (>) - the symbol used to compare 2 numbers when the larger number is on the left (21 > 13 means 21 is greater than 13)

Level 3

H

half/halves - one of two equal parts in a whole

half hour - a period of time equal to half of one hour; 30 minutes

half inch - a measure of length equal to half of one inch

hexagon - a polygon with six sides and six angles

hour (hr) - a unit used to measure time

hour hand - the shorter hand on a clock that points to the hour; the hour hand moves around the clock one time every 12 hours

I

identity property of addition - the property which states that the sum of any number and zero is that number
$$4 + 0 = 4 \qquad 0 + x = x$$

identity property of multiplication - the property which states that the product of 1 and any factor is the factor
$$6 \times 1 = 6 \qquad 1 \times 4 = 4$$

inch (in) - a customary unit used to measure length

inverse operations - operations that undo each other

K

key - the part of a map, picture, or diagram that shows what the symbols mean

kilogram (kg) - a metric unit used to measure mass

L

length - the distance from one end of an object to the other

less than (<) - the symbol used to compare two numbers when the smaller number is on the left (14 < 29 means 14 is less than 29.)

line - a straight path that extends infinitely in opposite directions

line plot - a graph that shows data on a number line with Xs

line segment - a part of a line with two endpoints

linear measure - a measure of length or distance

liquid volume - the amount or quantity of liquid in a container; capacity

liter (L) - a metric unit used to measure capacity

M

mass - the measure of the amount of matter in an object; gravity does not affect mass

milliliter (mL) - a metric unit used to measure capacity

minute (min) - a unit of time

minute hand - the longer hand on a clock that points to the minute; the minute hand moves around the clock one time every hour

multiple - the product of a given number and any whole number

multiplication - the operation using repeated addition of the same number; combining equal groups

multiply - to join or combine equal groups

N

number line - a line on which points correspond to numbers

numerator - the top number in a fraction; how many equal parts are being considered

O

o'clock - a label used to indicate time; o'clock is a contraction for "of the clock"

octagon - a polygon with eight sides and eight angles

odd number - a whole number that ends in 1, 3, 5, 7, or 9

operation - an arithmetic procedure used to solve a mathematical problem, such as addition, subtraction, multiplication, or division

order of operations - the order in which the operations are completed within an expression:
1. parentheses
2. multiplication/division from left to right
3. addition/subtraction from left to right

P

parallelogram - a quadrilateral with opposite sides that are parallel and congruent

partition - to divide or separate a whole into parts

pattern - a regularly-repeated arrangement of numbers, letters, or shapes, etc.

pentagon - a polygon with five sides and five angles

perimeter - the distance around a closed figure

picture graph - a graph that uses pictures or symbols to represent collected data

place value - the value determined by the position of a digit in a number

plane figure - a flat shape that has only two dimensions, length and width

p.m. - after noon; the time between 12 noon and 12 midnight

point - an exact location in space

polygon - a closed figure made of line segments

product - the answer to a multiplication problem

Q

quadrilateral - a polygon with four sides and four angles

quarter hour - a period of time equal to one-fourth of an hour; 15 minutes

quarter inch - a measure of length equal to one-fourth of an inch

quotient - the answer to a division problem

R

reasonable - logical or sensible

rectangle - a polygon with four sides and four right angles

regroup - to rename a number 10 ones = 1 ten, 10 tens = 1 hundred

regular polygon - a polygon in which all sides are the same length and all angles have the same measure

 Level 3

remainder - the number left over after dividing into equal groups

rhombus - a parallelogram whose four sides are congruent and whose opposite angles are congruent

round - to estimate a number to the nearest ten, hundred, thousand, etc.

rule - a procedure that a pattern must follow

S

scale - (1) a tool used to measure weight or mass; (2) a number line with marks at fixed intervals used in graphing

side - one of the line segments that forms a polygon

sixth - one of six equal parts in a whole

square - a special rectangle with four sides of equal measure

square unit - a square with a side length of one unit that is used to measure area; square units may include square inch, square foot, square centimeter, and square meter

standard form - a way to write numbers using the digits 0-9 (1 hundred 5 tens and 3 ones is 153 in standard form.)

standard units - units of measure that are accepted as a standard (inch and centimeter are both standard units of linear measure)

subtraction - the operation of taking away part of a group or comparing the difference in the sizes of two groups

sum - the answer to an addition problem

T

table - information organized in columns and rows

tally chart - a chart or table used to record the count of something using tally marks

tally mark - a mark used to keep track of data being counted

third - one of three equal parts in a whole

time interval - the amount of time that passes between two events; time intervals may be measured in seconds, minutes, hours, days, weeks, etc.

trapezoid - a quadrilateral with one pair of parallel sides

triangle - a polygon with three sides and three angles

two-dimensional figure - a plane figure that has length and width

V

vertex/vertices - the point where 2 rays meet, where two sides of a polygon meet, or where the edges of a polyhedron meet; the top point of a cone or pyramid

W

whole - a shape or a set that is complete with no parts missing

whole numbers - the set of counting numbers and zero

width - the measure or distance across something from one side to the other

Notes

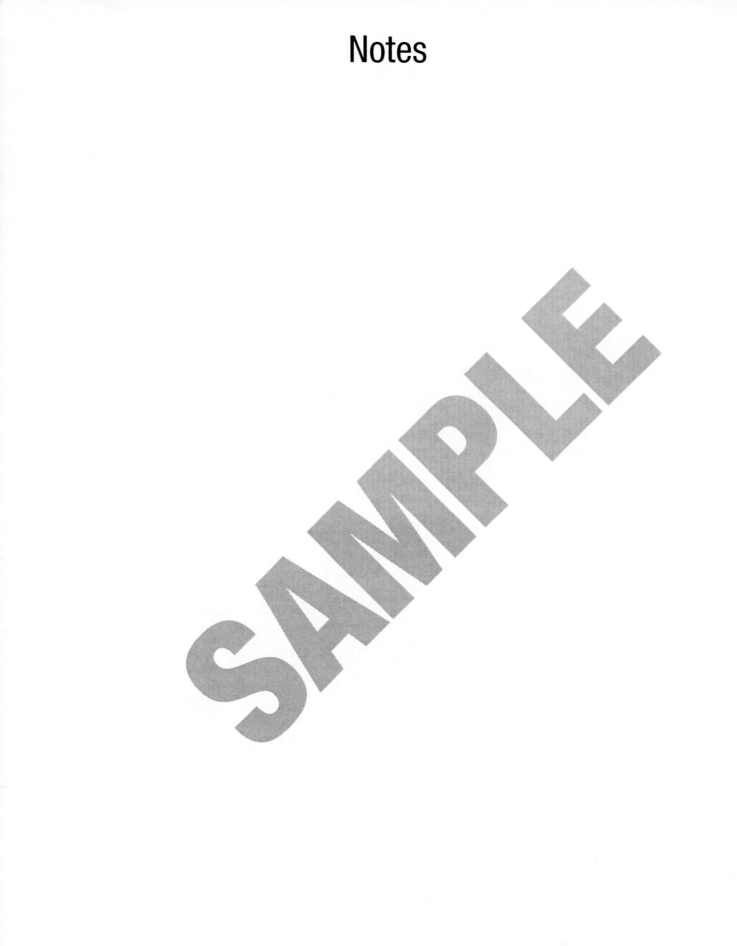

Level 3

GRADE 3
Mathematics Chart

TIME

365 days = 1 year

12 months = 1 year

52 weeks = 1 year

7 days = 1 week

24 hours = 1 day

60 minutes = 1 hour

60 seconds = 1 minute

LENGTH

Customary

3 feet = 1 yard

12 inches = 1 foot

Metric

100 centimeters = 1 meter

10 millimeters = 1 centimeter

Inches
0
1
2
3
4
5
6

GRADE 3
Mathematics Chart

LIQUID VOLUME (Capacity)

Metric

1000 milliliters = 1 liter

MASS

Metric

1000 grams = 1 kilogram

AREA

$A = l \times w$

20 19 18 17 16 15 14 13 12 11 10 9 8 7 6 5 4 3 2 1 0

Centimeters

Level 3

Notes

Notes

RR Donnelley Lewisville, TX USA June 2014 SAM17930